OIL PROPERTY VALUATION

Oil Property

Valuation

By

PAUL PAINE

NEW YORK

JOHN WILEY & SONS, Inc.

London: CHAPMAN & HALL, Limited

1942

PRINTED IN THE UNITED STATES OF AMERICA

PREFACE

Published accounts of the valuation of oil properties have been concerned chiefly with the important element of the oil and gas contents of lands. Less attention has been given to those other influences which affect the value of the oil and gas, to the various valuation methods appropriate to different circumstances, and to the forms in which oil properties occur.

The aim here is to help close that gap, especially for the younger engineers, with a review of the meaning and scope of valuation in the oil business, the factors which enter a valuation, and the methods of applying these. Questions which arise in valuation practice and the avenues of solution are discussed rather than efforts, in these days of rapid changes, to provide specific answers and detailed lists of equipment costs.

And thanks should be recorded here to H. K. Armstrong, Ernest K. Parks, and Robert Moore, who have done much to improve the original manuscript of this book.

PAUL PAINE

LOS ANGELES, CALIF.
August, 1942

CONTENTS

CHAPTER I

CHAPTER II

CHAPTER III

CHAPTER IV

Chapter V

The oil — Marketing — The gas — Casinghead gas and natural gasoline — Costs for acquisition, development, operations, taxes, and overhead — Present worth — Unit projects — Marginal properties.

Chapter VI

The engineering or analytical method — The payout — The daily barrel — The well as a unit — The barrel in the ground — For the lender — The royalty — Fair market value.

Chapter VII

The data — Examination — Accounting — The balance sheet — Profit and loss statement — The report — Contents — Check lists — Reports for regulatory bodies.

CHAPTER I
THE SCOPE OF VALUATION

The petroleum industry is the one circus bigger
inside the canvas than on the posters.
— *Sketches in Crude Oil,* by JOHN J. McLAURIN

The principal factors in the valuation of a producing oil property
are the estimates of (1) the recoverable oil; (2) the profits to be obtained from the extraction of this oil; (3) the resulting values under
various conditions. The value of nonproducing acreage is more
simply ascertained. This work is concerned with these topics, with
less emphasis on the subject of estimating the oil reserves.

Most of the recorded study relating to the subject has been directed
toward the estimation of the recoverable oil and gas, called the oil and
gas reserves, and has had its inception in tax situations and the accompanying accounting matters. The derivation of the worth of these
reserves, expressed in dollars, has received less attention. However,
the dollar values of oil properties have been of concern to the leaders
in the industry since its beginning. Before Colonel Drake put down
the first successful well that was drilled for oil in the United States, he
prevailed upon the landowners to reduce the royalty rate to one-third
of that stipulated originally in the lease.

In the United States of America 22 states produce oil and gas in
commercial quantities; some 3,500,000 acres of land are known to contain oil, and the major portion of this land is now developed and under
exploitation. Petroleum accounts for 15 per cent of the value of all
minerals produced in the United States. In addition, a total area in
excess of 100,000,000 acres is considered to hold sufficient prospects of
yielding production to have led the producing interests to acquire the
oil rights under lease and to pay rentals for this privilege. About 20
large oil companies, most of them being integrated and functioning in
all branches of the industry, produce half of the oil in the United
States. The other half is produced by about 18,000 operating units,
containing an extraordinary proportion of rugged individualists who
maintain an intense competitive spirit and capacity to disagree among

1

themselves. About half of the oil is produced from 2 per cent of the wells. Half of the 717,000 oil wells drilled since the beginning of the industry are still producing. The average yield per well is about 10 barrels per day.

The early days of the industry were those of wide profit margins, less competitive buying of properties than now. The companies were small and compact; an absence of mathematical formulas was compensated by the wisdom of mature and experienced minds. With modern growth of large organizations and their integration, the rapid depletion of new fields, and the shifting bases of supply have come companies of such size that entire units are occupied solely with the study of matters relating to the valuation of properties.

The objective here is to list and to describe those subjects which are of concern in the valuation of an oil property. The two forms in which such properties are encountered are those which are not proved to contain oil, but which are considered to have some prospects, and the proved properties, whether developed or not. Those topics which are considered in the examination of the second class are

1. The estimate of the recoverable oil and gas.

2. The factors or pieces of information which concern their value.

3. The methods of applying these factors, under the various conditions and in the light of the various purposes for which a valuation may be made.

The industry since its beginning has been concerned with attempts to measure the values of oil wells and of both prospective and producing oil properties. It was early recognized that the measurement had to do with a wasting asset. The developments were rapid and sensational to an extent that gave this particular industry a character very different from the calm and more orderly behavior of general industry. The activities and growth called for simple rules and their easy application, with a hoped-for wide margin of safety. This resulted in two widely applied yardsticks for measuring oil property values — value per acre and a value based on daily rate of production. Each in turn was closely related to the price of oil, or, at any rate, the value leaned heavily upon price. The rates per daily barrel of flow were low for flush production; they increased with the age and the " settled " condition of the wells.

In 1911–12 what was then considered to be a spectacular figure was reached at Glennpool, Oklahoma, when a unit rate of $100 per daily barrel of net production (after royalty) was adopted in a widespread competitive acquisition of many properties by several large companies. The unit rate gradually increased under the stimulus of advancing crude prices and the development of the natural gasoline industry until in the same district, during 1920, prices in excess of $4,000 per barrel of net daily production were paid.

The price of oil, a dominant factor, was then a genuine function of the relation between the consumption or market demand and the country-wide production. There was no holding back of production, except from a lack of pipe lines or tank cars in which to move the oil. The rate of production depended on the results of exploration, and they were then, as now, entirely unpredictable and never uniform. Withdrawal rates were especially high where small-unit operations were conducted on many tracts of small size.

The costs of production were of less consequence than they are to-day; taxes were negligible; and casinghead (natural) gasoline was almost valueless. A general standard of purchase aimed to have a property " payout " in 3 to 5 years. Careful buyers sought the older and more fully developed properties, having wells which had reached the settled stage. They could be measured more closely, and they were less mercurial than the newer properties. The latter class, containing a small number of high-initial flowing wells from a reservoir whose characteristics have not become known, has caused the bad trades as far as the purchasers have been concerned. Pumping production might have sold at times for what appeared to be high prices, but generally the wells had a way of eventually pumping their way out.

Conditions are now different. The purchase and use of various oils have become much more selective, since crude oils of the same gravity are widely different in quality. Costs have vastly increased. The financial centers have taken up the oil business. The competitive search for properties is more intense, in spite of the narrowed margin of profits. It is appropriate to consider the elements and the meaning of value.

Meaning of Value

" *Value*," said Justice Brandeis, " is a word of many meanings." Jerome Frank has described it as " a vague symbol of a variety of different things." Value seems to be the main theme in economics. The word, in fact, has been put to many uses and has been employed for many purposes; and this is unfortunate because the result has become a field day for adjectives. We hear of " real value," " true value," " exchange value," " forced sale value," " going concern value," " replacement value," " income value," " fair market value," " enterprise value," " intrinsic value."

Value, when expressed in terms of a general exchange unit, such as dollars, is *price.*

Valuation is the process of estimating the value of a property at a specific time, or as of a specific time. In a derived sense it is the result of an appraisal, and the terms are frequently considered to be synonymous. To some small extent in the oil business, the word " appraisal " has come to designate an examination which is more penetrating as to inventories and measurements than is implied in valuation, the latter being simply the value ascribed to a certain property, without any specific confirmation of the actual existence of the property.

" The power to command a price " is a favorite definition of value with economists. This is one way of saying that value of property is what it sells for, and this in turn depends both on the commodity itself and on the extent and the nature of the market for the commodity that is available to the owner.

In the great majority of valuations the fundamental objective is to ascertain that amount for which a property will sell in the market (here the appraiser merely searches out and correlates the records as to the values which others have registered through their own actual transactions), or to ascertain the particular value which a property may have to its owner or to a buyer (here the appraiser is placed squarely on his own because he must estimate the amounts himself instead of being a recorder of transactions).

Purpose

Any concept of the value of a thing and the processes for ascertaining that value are bound to be influenced by the particular purpose for which the appraisal is being carried out. A valuation is never an end in itself, but may be required for any one of many purposes. Probably the most important public concern with these purposes has grown out of public utility rate cases. Other proceedings for which valuations are made relate to property purchases and sales, to banking operations, to tax matters, to mergers of companies. The various purposes require that the approach to the consideration of the value of a property have a considerable degree of flexibility, so that the valuation may best serve the end for which it is made. A property may have a much greater worth to one type of owner than to another.

It is evident, therefore, that in a valuation the purpose is an early consideration and must serve as a guide. It is an integral part of the valuation. It affects the scope and the conclusions and should be as clearly stated at the outset as it is understood by the engineer, if for no other reason than to promote in an engineer that rare virtue of keeping his judgement from being warped by his desire to serve the interests of his client.

Purpose in valuation practice and the weight which it carries with the appraiser account as much as anything for the fact that the majority of the valuations of producing oil properties found in general circulation appears to be on the high side rather than on the low. This grows out of the fact that most valuations have been made at the instance of sellers or of brokers who require a report which is both a valuation and a description. Activities in the sales of properties, as well as in financing, featured either in the refunding of old security issues or in the issuance of new securities, usually occur during the cycles of high crude prices, of increasing demand for crude, and of better-than-average earnings.

The circumstances surrounding the ownership of a given property suggest another need for knowing the purpose of a valuation. The genuine value of a property to a company which continues to own and operate it is precisely and inflexibly controlled by those factors, such as price of oil, income from gas, operating expenses, and taxes, which are contained in the company records. These factors must be given great weight when the worth of the property to the owning company is considered. But the value of this same property may be entirely different to some prospective buyer who considers himself a better operator (as all do) or who may have facilities for disposing of the oil to better advantage. This is one reason, although a minor one, why so many different opinions of values of the same property appear at times. A striking example of this is seen in the spectacular sales of proved leaseholds in the Osage Indian Agency. There seems little doubt that the completely wild and unaccountable prices which obtained during 1919 and 1920 were inspired by misguided notions on the part of bidders as to the utility to them of the oil which they expected to produce and to sell.

THE SPECIFIC DATE

The next essential after the purpose of a valuation has been clearly defined is to fix the date of its application. It may be that no specific date is required, as in those valuations which are descriptive of current conditions or in those which are concerned with the outlook for earnings beginning with the time when the report is prepared and dated. But most valuations are not in these classes, and generally it is well to establish a certain time " as of " when the valuation is to apply. Mergers and consolidations, partitions, and many other transactions are generally fixed by agreement to become effective as of a certain time, and the valuations which accompany these are required to be " as of " that date. Inheritance tax matters require that the tax be computed on the basis of the value of the assets at the date of death or optionally on the date one year later. Controversial situations often relate to values of properties as well as to the conditions which obtained at previous dates or during certain periods.

It is always desirable, but seldom happens, that the valuation actually be prepared at or very near to the time in question. The considerations which must be taken into account are then less confusing than at a later date when the situation has changed and the additional available information tangles the appraiser in his effort to differentiate between what he knows has happened and what he thinks he would have concluded at that time. The result of a valuation prepared concurrently with the time is more convincing and is especially more effective in legal proceedings.

More often, however, some time passes before the job is undertaken, and frequently a period of several years has elapsed. It then becomes necessary for the appraiser to keep in mind that he is not a prophet and that he must be guided by a strict adherence to the facts and to the apparent outlook as these facts appeared at the date " as of." Two sets of data need to be compiled and fully set out: (1) those which relate to the property and the surrounding developments at that time; (2) an account of the conditions, apart from the property, which obtained in the industry and which would have had an influence on a valuation.

The latter data are obtained from the trade journals and the newspapers. They include the schedules of crude oil prices, the regional developments and the scenes of activity, important transactions, trends in market demand. In theory at least, it is obligatory to rely solely on the facts as they appeared at that time and to refrain from any consideration of what has since been ascertained both as to the property and as to the industry in general. At best this is difficult, and it becomes increasingly so when the valuation is prepared for presentation in a controversy. It is particularly awkward and unhappy when the appraiser finds that the report which he would have made at the date in question contains conclusions and findings which have since been proved erroneous. Then, if these erroneous conclusions happen to coincide with the best interests of his client, the appraiser has need of all the ammunition he can bring to bear if his argument is to carry weight. He will require a thorough compilation of all the facts and a clear-cut account of the reasoning which led him to his conclusions.

If the appraiser does fail to avoid a partisan attitude, the influence of these obvious agencies can result in a valuation which may be difficult to defend later, during periods of lower prices, lessened activity, and cold scrutiny.

Classes of Valuations

Whatever the purpose of a valuation, and even if an account of its purpose has been omitted, it is occupied throughout with a determination of the utility or adaptability of a property and with a determination of its capacity to earn. It must be assumed that acquisition was pointed toward making use of the property and that such use is counted on to take the form of a profit, either directly or indirectly. Aristotle pointed out the comparison of the utility of a thing when put to its purposeful use in contrast with its use when exchanged for some other thing. Recently Locke has defined the use purpose as " intrinsic value "; the exchange use he calls " market value."

Four general classes comprise most oil-field valuations, grouped according to their functions.

1. As Security for Loans. One class is prepared in connection with routine banking operations, open account loans, and matters of that nature. They are not complete valuations in the real sense of the word because they rarely involve a thorough study of all the features which go to make up the full value of a property. Their concern is with the current and the early earnings, the requirements for capital expenditures, and the cash balances which will be available for meeting interest payments and sinking fund requirements. The possibility of deeper undeveloped sands under a producing property and the ownership of proven undeveloped holdings, even of oil reserves greatly out of proportion to the current rate of production, are of consequence in showing the borrower to have a backlog of assets, and this appeals to the lender. But these features count for relatively little in considering the merits of a short-term loan as compared with the prospects for cash profits during the period of the loan. The lender wants to measure the prospects that the loan will be paid when due. His vigilance seeks to avoid finding himself projected unwillingly into the oil-producing business.

2. Company Transactions. Operating companies buy and sell properties among themselves. They have come to do this increasingly during recent years in an effort to reduce the number of partnership and divided-interest holdings and in this way eliminate accounting expense and the inevitable inharmonies which grow out of conflicting ideas regarding operating procedures. Occasionally a merger is carried out. Sometimes accounting problems require a new presentation of the values of certain properties. Even the dissolution of a company may encounter the occasional recalcitrant stockholder who objects to the plan and brings a court action which requires an examination of the company assets. However, the most important valuations in this class are those occasioned by the purchase and sale of properties among companies, especially during the early days of a new and flush field. In addition, a part of the routine work of the appraisal departments in large companies is keeping what is equivalent to a continuing inventory valuation of their own properties.

3. Financing and Sale. This class is encountered in connection with matters of finance, whether of companies or of individual buyers and sellers. Such valuations receive public attention more than others; they are the most widely circulated, and they cover a wide range. They may relate to a bond issue of large size, where the property values run into many millions of dollars, or they may be a form of " report " prepared at the instance of a broker, promoter, or owner-seller who in the guise of a valuation is procuring what is really a description of the property, presumably from an unbiased source, but so closely connected with the genuine objective of the client that the appraiser must call on his whole power of resistance if he is to maintain an aloof and objective attitude.

4. Government Matters. Government matters consist of the large number of reports of values made necessary by governmental situations. They include mineral land value taxes, the write-offs for depreciation and depletion in computing the profits subject to income taxes, and property values subject to inheritance and gift taxes. The various administrative agencies have different ideas of what data they demand and of the form to be taken in their arrangement.

VALUATION METHODS

Any determination of value starts with a recognition of the purpose for which it is made and of the specific time. A conclusion concerning the method to be used in ascertaining the defined value follows. Several methods of appraisal have been in common use. It is apparent that some have little utility in oil-field practice.

1. **Actual Cost of the Property.** Original cost is relatively easy to ascertain, and the records provide it with specific and definite character. But in the oil fields the values change too rapidly for cost to have any significance except as an indication of what some one thought of the property on the day of sale.

2. **Estimated Replacement Cost, Less Depreciation.** Replacement cost is very seldom workable for oil properties. No two properties are precisely alike, nor are any two wells identical even though situated on the same property. Occasionally a question will arise about the replacement at any given time of a situation similar to the one in question or similar to the cost of acquiring a position with respect to acreage, having comparable prospects and merit.

3. **Actual Sales of the Same or of Similar Properties.** Sales of the same or of similar properties do provide a means of valuation which can be followed on many occasions for oil properties. This subject is discussed under Fair Market Value.

4. **Capitalization of Income Derivable from the Property.** The capitalization of income derivable from a property provides a theoretical approach which has been the basis of most oil-producing property valuations. This is the so-called " engineering " or analytical appraisal. It requires recognition, however, of the fact that each barrel of oil produced is a nonreplaceable unit of the capital account. In general, it is any procedure where the value of the property is reached by either a fixed calculation or an estimate of the income which it will provide.

This use of the expected income as a basis for the determination of value has been developed to a high degree in investment experience with all classes of property. It has been used widely in their purchase and sale. It found ready acceptance and application in oil-field practice, especially when so modified as to conform to the liquidating nature of a producing property and to the need to set up a measure of the present worth of deferred income through the application of appropriate discounts.

RELATION OF THE APPRAISER TO HIS EMPLOYER

Clients should be made aware that a valuation involves assumptions and estimates to such a great degree that exactness and precision must not be expected. The appraiser, on the other hand, should be prepared to supply advice and guidance on matters concerning which he has become informed through the examination and study which he has conducted. These topics may extend to many features beyond the formal matter contained in a report.

The confidential position in which the appraiser is placed charges him with a continued guarding of the information he has received and of the report he has rendered. They belong to the client; they are not the property of the engineer. For this reason he should explore at the outset the field of an engagement, ascertain if acceptance of the job is in conflict with any other commitment.

The future must be considered as well, for appraisals lead into strange paths. If the work is concerned with a controversial matter, arrangements should be made in advance for the position of the engineer when and if his findings should disagree with the best interests of his client. The extent and period of consulting and advisory service should be arranged if possible. Many relationships are so well established and of such long standing that preliminary agreements are unnecessary. Generally, however, a complete understanding in advance is essential in the interest of harmony. Examinations and reports, made in connection with the filing of proposals to sell securities with the securities commissioners of the states and with the Federal Securities and Exchange Commission, may draw the engineer in much deeper than he anticipated, and he may find himself interrogated about matters which he either does not want to discuss or feels that he cannot discuss without violating confidences.

It has been suggested that the engineer's position is comparable to that of an attorney with his client, and that view may be warranted under the statutes of some states. In others it is not so, the lawyers having cared for themselves and the doctors in this regard, but not the engineers. In any event, and whatever may be the reading of the law, its protection is of little benefit when the engineer confronts a governmental bureau or a state administrative agency which requires either a reply " or else."

A client does have a right to be informed about some measure of the upper and the lower limits within which an estimate may fall and about the relative importance and weights of the different elements which contribute to this uncertainty. He may then, if he wishes, arrange these variables in his own mind and conclude how much of a risk is run in accepting and relying on the appraiser in the dual role of engineer and economist, considered in the light of the original purpose which has occasioned the valuation.

It is evident, of course, that these features should apply only to the form and presentation of the conclusions rather than to the mechanics of the valuation itself. It follows that the introduction into the body of a valuation of such artificial hedges as " factors of safety " is not a genuine contribution toward accuracy. The most common form taken by such deliberate departures from accuracy is the doubtful virtue of " conservatism." The client should be handed the facts, the estimates, and conclusions, all free of misrepresentation, and be permitted to write his own ticket of protective measures. Confusion and misinterpretations are inevitable if a course toward exactness is charted and is ended in conservatism, unless the engineer has pointed out with unmistakable clarity the extent to which the pursuit of conservatism in an excess of carefulness or fear has led him away from what deep down in his heart he genuinely considers to be the correct estimate or answer.

Thus it appears that the valuation of an oil property may have to take into account matters which relate to economics, law, statistics, and accounting, as well as all those features of the technique of drilling and oil production that are peculiar to the highly specialized nature of this limited field.

The oil-field appraiser has an interesting and responsible scope of activity. No two situations are exactly alike. He has benefited if his observations have been widespread because, no matter how deep and penetrating he would have you think his examination of a property has been, one of the most effective tools he has brought into play has been a comparison of the property before him with other similar properties he has encountered elsewhere, whose histories he has followed. He has gained the " feel " of the various types of oil occurrences and the significance of the behavior of wells, and thereby reenacts those experiences and observations in the light of his diagnosis of the present problem.

He must be patient and sympathetic, unhurried in his contacts with field men, a good listener, not critical of operations as he finds them, disposed to learn and, above all, to cast the mantle of charity over what he considers the weaknesses of others.

REFERENCES

F. M. BABCOCK, *The Valuation of Real Estate,* 1932.
MAX BALL, *This Fascinating Oil Business,* 1940.
JAMES C. BONBRIGHT, *The Valuation of Property,* 1937.
Encyclopedia of the Social Sciences, 1934.
SAMUEL H. GLASSMIRE, *Law of Oil and Gas Leases and Royalties,* 1938.
J. A. GRIMES and W. H. CRAIGUE, *Principles of Valuation,* 1928.
JOHNSON, HUNTLEY, and SOMERS, *Business of Oil Production,* 1922.

JOHN J. MCLAURIN, *Sketches in Crude Oil,* 1896.
CAMPBELL OSBORNE, *Oil Economics,* 1932.
JOSEPH E. POGUE, *Economics of Petroleum,* 1921.
W. W. THORNTON, *The Law of Oil and Gas,* 1932.
C. M. WALSH, *The Four Kinds of Economic Value,* 1926.
WILLIAM WRIGHT, *The Oil Regions of Pennsylvania,* 1865.

CHAPTER II
PROPERTIES

The many different kinds of oil properties, the shapes taken by them, and the various purposes for which valuations are prepared preclude any formalized appraisal procedure that is applicable to all occasions. Properties do fall into different classes, and a review of the varied forms in which they occur is suggestive of the problems encountered in valuation practice since the valuation must take account of two primary considerations, (1) the physical nature or character or type; (2) the kind of title or ownership through which the property is held.

CLASSES OF PROPERTY

Lands
- Unproved
- Proved
  - Developed
    - Flowing
    - Pumping
    - Gas
    - Condensate
  - Undrilled

A more common classification of lands divides these classes into " producing " and " nonproducing," but this fails to identify as a separately important class those areas which are proved to contain oil but which are as yet undrilled. The great majority of property units in the United States is contained in that large class of unproved prospective lands held under leasehold by the operating companies. The high money values are in the smaller group of proved and producing properties which supply the current daily production of 4,000,000 barrels of oil and 3½ billion cubic feet of gas.

The simplest division of properties is, therefore, into those properties which are unproved and those which are proved (whether drilled or undrilled) ; and that is the standard appraisal arrangement. It is true that a property may be " proved " to be barren or unproductive; but the orthodox use of the term in the oil business is affirmative. Proved land means land that is either now actually producing or assuredly could be drilled profitably for its oil or gas production.

13

Proved Lands. Since "proof" is quite relative and entirely a matter of definition, considerable leeway exists among engineers as to those features and characteristics which establish land as definitely proved. Some restrict the term to only that acreage which has been pierced by the drill and whose drainage is considered to be tributary to completed wells. Others invoke a very tenuous combination of geology and imagination. The obvious result is a thin measure of proof, frowned on by those engineers who are more meticulous and who accordingly count themselves to be more ethical. There is no rule. A middle ground which appears to be reasonable and yet not severe has aptly been defined as that land where the oil is proved " to a high degree of probability."

Proved lands may be found to be developed fully or only partially. The extent of proved land that is undrilled at any certain time is determined chiefly by the relation of discoveries of new sources of supply to the amount of crude being currently produced. The introduction of new ideas and methods of exploring for oil brings about a cycle of discoveries of new fields. At first the discoveries are numerous, the new supplies of crude thus found exceed the withdrawals, and the ratio of proved acres that are undrilled to those which are drilled increases. Later, when the discoveries have slowed down during the phase when the geologists are not so rapidly turning up new structures, these tracts become drilled. Then some new exploration device is found, or a new theory of accumulation on which to explore, and the cycle is repeated. During recent years the discoveries have predominated, with attendant increases in the acreage that is proved but not drilled.

During periods of under-production and higher crude prices the development of vacant areas is intensified. Over-production of crude and a softening in the demand slows down the drilling.

One form of proved property which can exist but is seldom encountered is that which contains a few wells which outline the field. It is completely closed down and awaiting some future time for exploitation. Rarely is it possible to control an area so that competitive operations and lease requirements permit doing this. An oil company may acquire a large tract and then defer a test of it as long as the terms of the lease allow. But experience has shown that once an exploratory well has demonstrated the presence of oil, exploitation follows even where the entire control is held by a single operator. There is no setting aside for some future and more advantageous use. Experiments in this direction appear to have been unprofitable.

The type of oil occurrence as well as other causes affect both the development and the operation of a property. The productivity of a sand, its gas content, and the situation with respect to competitive offset land ownerships illustrate the kinds of factors which influence the spacing of wells and the equipment. They have led to the condition of the property as the appraiser encounters it. Frequently it is found that the well spacing has failed to conform to ideal practice and that the physical facilities are inadequate. The latter inadequacies can be changed to some extent, but the wells must remain where they are.

Unproved Lands. Unproved lands are those which are not known to contain oil but which by reason of the geological conditions are considered to have some prospect of becoming productive. Studying them and their acquisition is the chief occupation of the geological and leasing departments of an oil company. Usually the acquisition is in the form of an oil-and-gas lease, the lessee to pay the costs of development and operation and the lessor to receive a stated royalty portion of the income at no cost to him.

The oil business is never static, and producing companies either grow or decline to the extent that they discover or acquire newly proved tracts. These tracts are then developed, and this development is followed by a decline in the rate of production which in turn brings on a search for more properties. Without planned expansion and persistent effort to maintain reserves and an income rate, the producing company becomes a liquidating concern. No reasonable objection can be held if such is the deliberate policy of the owners, but it is unusual. In the oil-producing business the production rate seldom corresponds to demand; future supply conditions cannot be forecast. The search for new sources of oil and the production of this oil are carried out under conditions which are unpredictable and widely different from those found in other industries. A producing company is better fortified for the future if it has a well-chosen spread of promising, unproved acreage.

A producing oil company, considered as a going concern, is strengthened if some balance is found to exist in the extent of its proved and productive lands and of its lands which are unproved. No two situations in this regard are alike, and all acreage tracts vary widely in quality. A good average workable ratio of land holdings in an alert and progressive producing company is about 40 acres of unproved leaseholds per daily barrel of production or per acre of proved and producing land. This is nothing more than a general and suggestive comparison, never to be strictly applied to any specific situation, but mentioned here for the purpose of emphasizing the difference between the companies which are adventuring into new areas and those which seek no further expansion. In the appraisal of an oil company this is a feature of consequence; it should be identified and described.

Such an inquiry has no place in an appraisal which concerns a single tract or defined area. There the test is the value of a specific piece of land. It is dangerous to do more than suggest the point of view as to a widespread acreage position, for many successes of operators who have deviated from this rule and have held only small tracts of land demonstrate that good fortune in the oil business is often achieved through chance and even through an erroneous line of reasoning. The business is saturated with bewildering incongruities.

The character of lands has much to do with their utility to an operating oil company. They may be well chosen for their situation, both along major geological trends and in the vicinity of test wells. On the other hand, they may be carelessly selected, without consistent policy and reasons, with a resulting land-record file that is immediately apparent to the appraiser because it is aimless. The tracts are unrelated, not well distributed, and fail to indicate a clearly reasoned program. It is true that each individual piece of land may be appraised with a well-considered value, and yet the picture as an entity and going concern can be either good or bad in regard to a reasonable expectation of benefiting from the results of exploration. This factor is of consequence in the valuation of a company.

PROVED LANDS

Proved Properties. The proved property which is known to contain oil or gas is found in many stages of development. It may be entirely undeveloped and yet be so sufficiently tested by nearby wells and the known geological conditions that no reasonable doubt can be held about its productivity. Or it may be either partially or fully developed with wells. Many varieties are examined at one time or another. About 390,000, or nearly one-half of the 759,000 producing oil wells that have been completed in the United States since the inception of the business in 1859 are still producing.

Properties containing recently completed flowing oil wells are, of course, those which have the most uncertain outlook. They demand a cool and dispassionate study by the appraiser. Fortunately the much improved methods for ascertaining reservoir and sand conditions have vastly clarified many features which formerly were the subject of little better than guesswork. Such features have now become definitive, particularly in the field of core sampling and in the analysis and study of cores. Electric logging supplements cores and provides a particularly useful means of correlating subsurface strata. Bottom-hole pressure records, subsurface thermometers, and a host of new devices enable an early determination of the characteristics of a new field and the effect upon it after the early oil withdrawals.

Pumping wells are less spectacular, but they comprise the backbone of the industry. They range in depth from the very shallow wells of a few hundred feet to the wells of several thousand feet; from the small " stripper " wells which yield a fraction of one barrel per day to the wells which pump large volumes; from wells which pump only clean oil to wells which lift a fluid that is 95 per cent water. Variations occur in the nature, weight, and viscosity of the oil, the proportion of gas which accompanies it, and the extent of sand cavings.

The results of these variations are operating conditions and lifting costs which range from a few cents per barrel to several dollars per barrel. Relatively few pumping wells are operated for lifting costs less than 7 cents per barrel; and the commercial limit on the high side is about 60 cents, except in situations where the gas sales or high casinghead gasoline recoveries and low royalty rates combine to create a situation where the oil itself may cost more to obtain than its value, and the profit be provided by the byproducts.

Forms of Oil Properties

This business of searching for and producing crude oil is unique in many respects. Oil deposits are elusive and difficult to find, and when found they frequently fail to return a profit. The unpredictable nature of discoveries has made the search highly speculative and has given its history much romance and glamor. The rewards have to be great in order to compensate for the risks. The business occupies a unique and isolated place in industry. It has to do with a product that is migratory; it requires specialized equipment, knowledge, and experience. The resultant holdings take unusual forms, not only in their physical nature but also in the types of ownership.

In the United States the oil belongs to the owner of the land underneath which it is situated. But it passes to the person who reduces it to possession. This is the law of capture. It is not surprising, therefore, that oil-field scenes in a newly discovered field are far from calm and sedate. It is not a leisurely business. The development must be active and aggressive; almost any amount of capital expenditure is warranted in preference to the loss of oil by drainage to contiguous or nearby tracts of land.

Ownership in Fee. Ownership in fee means the full ownership of the entire property, comprising all the surface and underground rights, without any segregation of interest. It is reflected in the wording of some old deeds which register conveyance of a property and of everything thereto pertaining " as high as heaven and as deep as hell." It is the simplest type of property title encountered by the oil man, and he immediately undertakes to divide and complicate it. Full fees are seldom in the portfolios of oil companies because the great majority of property acquisitions are in the form of a leasehold or rental agreement, described as an " oil-and-gas lease."

The word " fee " is rather carelessly used in the oil business, and it is well for the appraiser to be on his guard concerning the scope of this word because it has a variety of provincial meanings in different localities. In some districts it describes the ownership of minerals to the extent of the sole right to develop and produce them, but subject to a payment as if and when produced; in other words, equivalent to a perpetual lease without any obligation to drill or to pay rent. This use is obviously misleading to one not familiar with the local connotation of the term.

Mineral Rights. Legally the landowner owns the mineral and has the right to separate the ownership of subsurface mineral from the ownership of the land. Such a segregation of the minerals in the property from the ownership of the surface rights results in the mineral rights. A mineral deed conveys the minerals. The minerals produce the royalty; the royalty in turn arises from the lease. It should and generally does carry a right of entry to the property for the purpose of developing and producing the minerals, subject to reimbursement to the surface owner for damages to his crops. Sometimes the mineral reservation applies only to oil and gas. Sometimes it has been divided and a portion transferred under a conveyance whose terms restrict to one of the owners the exclusive right to execute a leasehold agreement. The remaining interest then becomes equivalent to a perpetual royalty in the oil and gas when produced but without any control over the lease and its provisions and with no participation in the bonus benefits received for the lease.

Royalty and mineral interests in Louisiana require special attention because the common law in that state differs from that of the other states in many respects. Undeveloped mineral rights cannot remain permanently dissociated from the surface ownership. There is no such thing as ownership of oil and gas in place separate and apart from the land. The only right which can be assigned is the right to procure the minerals. Such right is called a " servitude," is not a perpetual transfer of ownership, and must be exercised within ten years.

Surface Rights. Ownership in the surface rights of unproved prospective lands is seldom purchased by lessees, and it is an unusual item in a list of company assets. The capital requirements for this would be quite beyond the resources of oil companies, which after all have no concern with surface ownerships except to the extent required for the conduct of oil operations. During periods when the prospects for oil are distant and uncertain, this ownership of surface has the nominal real estate value for farming and grazing that is reflected by current transactions in similar properties in the neighborhood. If the valuation is to be shaded either way as to a tract which continues in the ownership of an oil company, it should be on the down side because of the well-known incapacity of oil concerns to conduct farm operations efficiently.

When a tract has been proved for oil production and is being developed, its status is strengthened. A paradoxical situation results because a farm as such actually suffers when oil developments are conducted on it; it is worth less and yet the seller is able to exact more for it from the operating company if he makes a sufficient nuisance of himself. The rights of the mineral interest to drill and operate can interfere seriously with agricultural activities and thus lessen its usefulness to the owner. Some of this loss the owner can usually recover by reason of the terms of the lease. But, in addition, his assertion of claims for damage and, in general, his making a pest of himself can be carried to such an extent that he recovers handsomely in the long run on his nuisance position. Every cow that is hit by a truck was the best one in the herd. Every orange tree removed (21 trees are required for a well location) was a full-bearing tree that was rapidly paying off the farm mortgage.

The values of surface rights, therefore, vary greatly with the circumstances. Desert lands have no surface value of consequence. Ownership of the surface rights by an operator who also owns the oil wells and production rights is merely equivalent to ownership of another operating facility. This possession is reflected in the estimated costs and profits from the exploitation of the oil, and the value of the land itself need not ordinarily be segregated from the other equipment items which are used for the recovery of the oil over a considerable period of time. If the land happens to be of so unusual a nature that the present worth of its salvable condition is substantial enough to warrant consideration for that time in the future when the oil will have become exhausted, then some account may properly be taken of it; otherwise not.

An exception to the foregoing will be found to hold for most blue-sky valuations made for securities commissioners in various states. Commissions seem to attach enough importance to the record of equipment so that a rather itemized report of the physical facilities and their value is required. The surface rights should be included in such a list.

If the surface rights are in an alien hand when oil is discovered on a piece of land, then the value of the surface is a function of its utility to the oil operator, and the element of need or necessity plays an important part. A tract of land which is to be used for a natural gasoline plant, a tank farm, a central power plant, or a compressor station permits considerable flexibility of choice because no single, limited, specific plot is essential. Alternative sites usually may be found. But the surface ownership of an important piece of producing oil land unhappily represents a nuisance position, whose extent depends on the terms of the lease under which the property is to be developed, the improvements belonging to the surface owner, the nature of the oil operations, the density of well locations, the damage claims which may result from mishaps, and finally the staying qualities of each side in this not uncommon oil-field siege.

The Lease. The oil-and-gas lease records a delegation by the owner of the minerals, called the lessor, to a lessee of the right to develop and produce from the property, subject to a rental payment of either money and/or a portion of the output. Strictly speaking, it is not a lease as that term is generally used but is a grant of the minerals as such, along with the exclusive rights to mine them. In the United States the lease as an instrument is older than the oil-field well. In 1853, J. D. Angier of Cherrytree Township, Venango County, Pennsylvania, agreed to

> repair and keep in order the old oilspring on land in said Cherrytree Township, or dig and make new springs and the expenses to be deducted out of the proceeds of the oil and the balance, if any, to be equally divided, the one-half to J. D. Angier and the other half to Brewer, Watson & Co., for the full term of five years from this date, if profitable.

But the experiment did not pay, and Mr. Angier ceased to be an oil man.

In the summer of 1856, a Mr. Bissell conceived the idea of drilling for oil in Oil Creek. The property had been leased for 99 years to Pennsylvania Rock Oil Company, which in turn, late in 1856, sub-

leased it to a Wall Street broker, named Havens, for a $500 bonus
and an agreement to pay " 12 cents a gallon for all oil raised for 15
years." This appears to have been the first oil lease in the United
States that carried a royalty. This lease expired by default, Mr.
Havens having failed to conduct any drilling operations. Later, on
the same property, was drilled the Drake Oil Well.

It seldom happens that title to the entire fee ownership of a property,
or even to the entire mineral interest in it, is held by the operator
who produces the oil. The great majority of producing units are
operated under rights provided by the lease. This is usually a simple
printed document, the terms of which have come to have meanings well
established through many court adjudications. An actual documentary lease must be in existence if a valuation is to be acceptable.
Under certain conditions a short-term lease may be verbal, but any
oil-and-gas lease for a period of over one year must be in writing.

The form known widely as Producers 88 came into general use
throughout the Mid-Continent region and spread to other oil areas.
A great number of court decisions have clarified the meanings of its
content. Later various alterations pertaining to casinghead gas requirements, rentals, and other terms led to new forms designated 88–A,
88–B, etc. The trustworthy 88 has lost both meaning and character.
In fact, just the words " Form 88 " printed at an upper corner of a
lease form now suggests undesirable lessor conditions.

The *term* is for a specific period, usually from 2 to 5 years, then
expires if no production has been obtained. It requires usually that a
well be drilled or else requires, in lieu of drilling, the payment of
rentals (from 10 cents to $1.00 per acre) annually for the privilege of
delaying drilling operations from year to year during the term of
the lease. The rental is thus really penalty or delay money for failure
to drill. Nearly all leases contain the " thereafter " or habendum
clause which continues the lease in force so long thereafter as oil or gas
is produced in paying quantities, and subject to other terms and
conditions, such as

> Occasionally a lease is found with unconventional terms.
> Drilling rights may cease at the end of a period of years.
> The right to drill deeper may cease.
> Production rights may cease entirely, or they may continue but
> without the right to drill new wells or to redrill or to repair those
> already drilled.

A lease may be brought to an end through forfeiture by reason of
the lessee's failure to comply with its terms. This requires a legal

action brought by the lessor and is considered difficult to bring about except in cases of actual fraud or flagrant violations of the lease terms.

The *surrender clause* permits the lessee to relinquish the lease and thereby be relieved of any obligation for further development. From the operator's standpoint, this clause is an absolute essential, and its absence very seriously reduces the value of a lease, except in those instances where there is no prospect whatever that the lessee may wish to relinquish it. If not contained in a lease, it may have the effect of an actual obligation to drill a test well, to continue rental payments or other undesirable provisions from which the lessee has no means of release or escape. Its use in leases is so thoroughly general that the appraiser assumes that it is present. In the examination of a large number of properties he asks the land department merely to indicate in the list which leases, if any, fail to contain this clause. These leases, then, must be examined with care as to the implications and liabilities which result from this inability to let go.

Development requirements in the simple forms of leases call for an initial well, or the payment of rentals in lieu thereof, when no offset wells which presume drainage of the property exist. Once oil has been found and is being produced from wells situated on adjoining properties, the lease requires that offset wells shall be drilled when the competitive wells are within certain distances of the property line. The lease may contain considerable detail with respect to these offset requirements; if not, it has been well established under the law that a reasonable and proper development is implied as an obligation on the part of the lessee to drill and protect the property from drainage. The latter alternative to the more specific spelling out of requirements is often an advantage.

The more elaborate provisions for development stipulate the number of strings of tools to be kept at work continuously developing the property, require the drilling of one well to a specified number of acres, and compel a surrender of the undrilled acreage when the lessee terminates drilling. In general, the lessee is expected to develop and exploit the property in a workmanlike or "minerlike" manner. This feature is of particular concern to the appraiser because the lease may require expenses for drilling which exceed a normal budget for this purpose and may still fail to add materially to the amount of oil recovered.

Development, and at times production operations, may be suspended when the price of crude oil falls below some stated level. A lease contains the usual *force majeure* clause, as well as provision for the lessee's abiding with state laws regarding curtailment of production.

A lease may even permit the lessee to join in a general voluntary movement of the kind which has no statutory background.

Rental is due on inactive leaseholds, upwards from 10 cents per acre per year. One dollar per year per acre has been a general and widely used rate.

Gas. The older lease forms reflect the oil man's attitude at that time toward a gas well as toward a disagreeable relation — something which might not be definitely harmful but having little real merit. That point of view no longer applies. Natural gas has wide uses and many applications. A modern lease recites with considerable detail the requirements for the drilling and spacing of gas wells (usually 1 to every 160 acres). It may specify the measuring of gas removed from the property and the rate below which it may not be sold.

Casinghead gas provisions differ widely, usually stipulating that with the one-eighth or one-sixth royalty a portion of this gas shall be retained by the lessee to make up for his added costs incurred in the recovery of this byproduct.

Gas distillate is a still more recently recognized product of commercial value, obtained chiefly along the Texas-Louisiana Gulf Coast by lowering the pressure of gas and thereby causing a condensation of the oil which has been held in the gas in vapor phase.

Taxes. Mineral land taxes are usually assessed against the mineral interests in the ratable proportions of the lessor and lessee.

Dehydration. Most present-day leases provide that the lessor be charged with the costs of dehydrating his royalty portion of the wet oil. This treatment of emulsified crudes is necessary in order to make the oil acceptable to the pipe-line buyers. Although this is a departure from the old conception of the lessor portion of the proceeds from the sale of the oil and gas as free and clear of all charges, the dehydration clause has become so general that its presence in a lease is not unorthodox.

Assignment. The right to assign a leasehold is sometimes specifically withheld or made subject to the approval of the lessor. The value of a lease to the lessee is affected adversely whenever the right of assignment is missing and especially when the lessor interests or rights have been divided and sold to many small holders. Assignment then becomes very difficult to arrange, and the lease ceases to meet banking requirements as collateral.

The *community lease* arises from situations where the property ownerships are in many tracts, usually so small that no single one is large enough to warrant a well, or where there may be a legal prohibition against drilling on tracts of less than a certain minimum size. By combining a sufficient number of small tracts in a community lease, a development project can be worked out. Such leases are difficult to assemble, and it is rarely that a few " holdouts " do not leave vacant places in the tract.

These leases call for exceptional clearness and a freedom from need of later modifications and alterations. After the prospects for oil have become bright, and even before then during the inevitable excitement preliminary to a discovery, it is exceedingly difficult to prevail on all the members in such a group of lessors to consent to any changes in the lease. It is also essential that a single depositary be named to receive and distribute the royalties.

United States Government Leases. Under the Mineral Land Leasing Law of 1920, the title to oil and gas in the public domain remains in the United States government. Certain portions, not including national parks, national monuments, are subject to lease for the development and production of oil and gas under specified conditions. These conditions may include a bonus, an annual rental, and defined royalties.

A *prospecting permit* covers 2,560 acres, is granted for a 2-year period in areas outside the geologic structure of proved oil fields. Within the first year a well must be drilled to a depth of 500 feet, and within 2 years to 2,000 feet. Upon discovery, the lessee may receive a 5 per cent royalty lease for an area equal to one-quarter that contained in the permit, with a minimum of 160 acres. He also has a preferential right to lease the balance at a royalty rate to be designated by the Secretary of the Interior. Generally this takes the form of a sliding scale, beginning at $12\frac{1}{2}$ per cent and increasing with the productivity rate. Regulations issued by the United States General Land Office describe and control the operation requirements, and the administration of the lands is under the United States Geological Survey.

Several *states* and *Indian agencies* control lands which are leased for oil and gas development. They follow no uniform pattern for lease requirements, royalty rates, or operating practices.

Contingent Payments Out of Oil. These payments are a liability against a property or a leasehold. Their origin is usually in some transfer of the leasehold where the sale has been made for a certain sum plus some certain additional sum to be paid from the sales of oil and gas if and when produced. It generally reflects some sort of compromise in the negotiations between the seller and the buyer which has taken a final form that leaves the ultimate amount to be paid dependent on the total oil produced. Most of the time this is a percentage of the production until a specific amount has been paid. If the full amount is never supplied out of the production, then its effect is equivalent to that of an overriding royalty. In a valuation it may be encountered in the form of a charge against the operating interest which is being appraised. Or it may be held as an asset which is being dealt in, by reason of having come into the hands of brokers as commissions. It requires specific consideration, as well as estimates of the extent and timing of these additional payments, in order to ascertain their estimated worth if held separately or their effect on a property value if the property value is being appraised.

When so contingent an obligation is found to be an item in the title file of an unproved leasehold, or in any other instances where the appraisal is not based upon an estimate of recoverable oil, the measure of its adverse effect on a property value cannot be computed definitively. It does affect the fair value, and the extent of this is a matter of judgement and opinion. Contingent payments of this kind are bought and sold actively in areas where there appears some likelihood of the properties' becoming productive even though the lands are not definitely proved.

The Carried Interest. Attached to the title files of many oil-and-gas leases are records of contingent beneficial interests, under the terms of which the beneficiary is to receive a portion of the profits gained by the lessee. Generally this is to become effective when the property has " paid out "; that is, after the operator has had returned to him from the sales of oil and gas an amount equal to his cash expenditures, or some other specific amount. Less often, but occasionally, it is specified that the carried interest is to be on the earnings as computed by capitalizing the development costs and retiring them through appropriate charges to depreciation in the profit-and-loss determination. This puts the holder of the interest into the money at an earlier point, but does not increase his ultimate return unless the property should fail to pay out on a cash-in, cash-out basis. Variations in this type of deal restrict or specify the amounts which may be charged for various portions of the costs of oil recovery, such as supervision and overhead, and even costs for lifting and field operations. Carried interests may be for one well on a property or for the entire property.

This element is either an asset or a liability, depending on whether it is considered from the standpoint of the operator or the beneficiary; it is wholly a contingent one as far as it concerns unproved lands and producing properties which have not yet reached the payout point. Accordingly, it is not usually revealed in a balance sheet, and quite likely is not part of the lease document. Actual existence of such obligations is easily overlooked if they are not specifically asked for, and any failure to disclose, on the part of those who have been charged with listing the property, is explained on the theory that the appraiser is concerned with the property and not the title. It is wise when examining properties to inquire about outstanding interests of this kind (as well as about the contingent payments out of oil) and, if they do exist, to ascertain their status and to take them into account as an element in the valuation procedure.

The range of importance on an interest of this kind can be wide — from being almost a negligible factor in the class of acreage whose prospects for oil are considered to be little better than nil, up to great consequence in proved and developed properties which have reached a point where the effect is equivalent to a partnership, except that the carried interest usually fails to have any voice in the management and conduct of operations. A favorite device of land brokers and dealers is to take a portion of their profits in the form of such a carried interest, which then reach the market through the dealers' selling interests in their interests.

The Fractional Interest. Partnerships are mixed blessings. They provoke much dissension, lost motion, and occasionally improved operations but just as often a series of inharmonies and wranglings that affect adversely the efficient operation of a property. Rarely is an oil-development operation handled to the satisfaction of all those who own interests. A valuation may be charged with inquiring the extent to which profits are affected by this discord. If the entire property is being appraised, the matter is of less concern because the test then becomes largely one of the potentialities of it in the hands of its proposed new owner. If a fractional interest is being appraised, and this interest has the control of the operations, and if the appraiser approves the operating methods, he can feel better than when he finds that the interest holds only an ownership contract, with the exclusive management in the hands of a partner who is unsatisfactory because of any one of many reasons. Among these reasons are untrustworthiness, common inefficiency, or the complex differences which grow out of the fact that their interests are not mutual. Such a divergence often exists between partners.

It is small comfort to the operator who finds himself excluded from active participation if his contract provides a right to " consult, confer, and advise "; the practical difficulties in the way of correcting a bad situation are almost insurmountable except when fraud is obvious and can be conclusively proved. It is more satisfactory to find that the operating contract requires approval of all interests to the drilling of new wells, to expenditures amounting to a certain sum, to the choice of a foreman, etc.

Other features can affect the desirability and the value of a fractional interest. Conversely, it may have an increased value to some interest by reason of its utility, entirely apart from the obvious earnings. Companies which have associated pipe lines and crude-oil purchasing concerns favor the ownership of such interests because they generally control the right to purchase the entire crude output, thus through this arrangement extending their pipe-line connections at a minimum of expense.

The Drilling Contract. An astonishing number and variety of deals are made during the development of a town-lot oil field, where small tracts of irregular shape provide many well locations. The owners are difficult to deal with, and the rights to drill are not so readily acquired by the ponderous land departments of large oil companies as against the competition of the small aggressive and resourceful promoter. He in turn may lack cash, but he creates transactions in a wide range, based on the fundamental requirement that some one else put up the money and equipment with which to drill the well. This may take the form of a cash contribution or a drilling contractor may undertake the work for an interest; some one may supply the casing or loan the derrick and drill pipe for an interest, or pay for half the fuel, etc.

The interests thereby obtained may be in the form of an overriding royalty or of a portion of the working interest. If it is a royalty, it may be perpetual or it may have a ceiling after which it ceases. These dealings are known collectively as drilling contracts. They cross the appraiser's path because the participants are ubiquitous and welcome borrowers from banks.

Another form of drilling contract has reached into higher places. This form had its origin in those districts where curtailment had been so severe that a return of the well costs from its profits required from 3 to 6 years or longer. Formerly a few well completions might have provided enough income to care for the continued development outlay, but now the oil company finds itself holding as lessee a large body of proved acreage, and is confronted with a fixed obligation to develop it. If the company lacks sufficient resources to meet this need, or if it wishes to divert its cash and income elsewhere and still does not want to borrow or to extend its capital structure, it arranges with a drilling contractor to drill the wells and to take his pay out of the major portion of the working-interest production until the well charges plus interest have been liquidated.   The program is predicated on sure-shot well locations; dry holes are paid for in cash on completion.

In the examination of the various forms of drilling contract situations, the appraiser becomes concerned with the scope of the contract terms as much as with matters relating to the oil wells.   The effects of accounting practices as to whether the contractor or the company can take depreciation allowances against income reacts on the important feature of future income tax charges.   Since the obligation to pay for the wells may be construed under some circumstances as a contingent one, payable out of oil, it may be that the obligation does not find its way into the company balance sheet.

The Unit Project.   Unitization is a pooling of interests, and over 150 unit projects are now in effect in the United States.   The unit project places control and direction of oil and gas operations over a number of contiguous properties under one directing agency.   The operations are handled as an entity, the participation, costs and income being based on agreed rates or measures, such as area, estimated reserves, well locations, acre-feet of productive sand.   The theory of the unit project contemplates that, by thus coordinating the conduct of the field operations, all the interests and owners therein will share ratably and to better advantage than if each were to operate quite independently of the other.   The determination of this ratable participation and interest usually takes the form of a long and tedious series of maneuvers and disagreements which leave no one very happy with the outcome.

However, the unit project as an advance in the utilization of a great natural resource has proved its worth so thoroughly in the form of increased recoveries, better control of output, and lower costs that the chief objections raised appear to be by those whose individual interests would be adversely affected through their being restrained from resorting to the law of capture and to an aggressive and capable ability to develop and produce ahead of the adjoining landowners.

In the past the course usually followed in a unit has been to assign definitely the title to properties held by the interests which comprise it; it is now considered to be more practicable for each member to retain ownership of his property, but to have delivered to him a continuing portion of the products recovered and for him to bear a like proportion of the expenditures.   The result takes the form of one large operation with obligations and benefits proportional to the interests.   The appraiser's problem starts with a consideration of the entire project, followed by an examination of the specific interest, and the prospect of its ratio of participation being changed by reason of the unit-formation agreement.

Many units are fixed in their extent and proportionate ownership. Others provide for some measure of flexibility and change from time to time as the subsequent exploration and development add to the knowledge of the size and importance of various areas either in or adjoining the participating tracts.

Many of the objectionable features which crop out in competitive drilling and production are avoided when the owners in a district merge their holdings and exploit the combined area in this single-unit form. The withdrawal of oil and gas is made more orderly; the control of reservoir conditions is more effective toward the recovery ultimately of more oil; and capital requirements for wells and the operating costs are reduced. It would be too much to say that all these highly desirable objectives have been achieved in every unit, and enough dissatisfaction has been expressed to suggest to the appraiser a need to examine carefully the conditions surrounding a unit interest which he is appraising.

Fundamentally the course is sound, and generally any great inequities are avoided. Many different plans of units have been devised; they are well explained in the *Handbook on Unitization of Oil Pools* of the Mid-Continent Oil and Gas Association.

The Royalty. The owner of land seldom desires to develop it for oil and gas himself; he prefers to lease it for that purpose, and he generally does so at some considerable time in advance of the time when the explorations demonstrate whether or not the land actually contains oil. He has received a payment or consideration for the lease, called a bonus, and since a very small proportion of leased tracts ever become productive this bonus not only is profit to the landowner but also may be his only return from this source. The leasing agreement is not really a lease in the usual sense of the word, but is a transfer of the property rights to the underground minerals, subject to a reservation to himself as lessor of a certain portion of these minerals, or of the proceeds from their sale, at no cost to him. This interest as lessor is the royalty. The lessee interest is called the working interest and, as its name implies, is the interest which is charged with the work as well as the expense of obtaining the oil and gas. A royalty always postulates a lease in which the royalty reservation is not to the oil and gas in place but to a portion of the oil and gas as they are produced.

In the United States it is not often that the oil operator is fortunate enough to own in entirety the property from which he produces oil, the proportion of the producing lands so owned in entirety being insignificant. Some 600,000 owners of lessor interests annually receive in excess of $200,000,000 for lease bonuses, rentals, and oil and gas royalty payments.

The royalty clause in the lease will contain the percentage of products allocated to the respective interests for oil, dry gas (sometimes called natural gas), casinghead gas, natural gasoline, and other products; the bases for the derivation of their values or for their accounting; the rights and/or obligations of the lessor to take his portion in kind.

Royalty owners are now more exacting and more fortunate than formerly. At Tidioute, Pennsylvania, in the early sixties, the Empire well yielded $12,000 in six days to the lessees. Its owners saved the oil and sold it for 10 cents per barrel. But the owners of the land were unable to furnish barrels; the royalty portion of the oil was put into pits, dug in the gravel, from which it escaped by seepage and was lost.

The royalty payment, as an obligation, is treated in some accounting methods as a direct charge against the cost of producing the oil; that is, as an expense. More often it is set up as a separate item which is credited to the lessor, and this conforms to the large proportion of court decisions which have generally held that the landowner's royalty portion of the oil continuously belongs to him, and for that reason the privilege of taking it, in kind, is always his even though the lease does not specifically so recite.

In most oil areas the universal royalty rate to the landowner is one-eighth of the oil and gas, or one-eighth of the proceeds received from the sale of the oil and gas. One-sixth is not an uncommon rate and may be said to be the prevailing rate in Ohio and California; it is also the rate effective for University lands in Texas. A royalty interest equivalent to one-eighth of the production from one acre is called a *royalty acre*. The one-eighth royalty interest in an 80-acre tract is equivalent to 80 royalty acres. A half interest in the one-eighth royalty from 80 acres is 40 royalty acres. In California another unit of measurement is used because royalty rates vary widely and also because there is much dealing in small divisions of royalty interests. This is the acre per cent, an interest equivalent to 1 per cent of the oil from 1 acre of land. A royalty acre equals $12\frac{1}{2}$ acre per cents. The foregoing owner of the one-eighth royalty from 80 acres owns 80 times $12\frac{1}{2}$, or 1,000 acre per cents. If he sells 50 acre per cents, the purchaser has acquired an undivided royalty interest in the gross oil produced from the 80 acres amounting to $(50)/(1,000) \times 0.125 = 0.00625$, or 0.625 per cent of the gross oil produced.

Many landowners are situated so that they should not take the entire gamble with their royalty interest, especially if this royalty interest is of such a nature that it would become valueless on the completion of one dry hole in the neighborhood. It is a common practice for the owners to divide and to sell for cash a half or some fractional part of the royalty. Note the difference here between selling an interest in the minerals in the property and selling an interest in the royalty which is tied into and related to a specific lease; when the lease expires the royalty expires also, and this leaves the land title clear.

Such fractional interests have been a favorite field for promotional activities. They become further divided until they reach microscopic sizes, especially those properties which are producing oil and yielding an income. The lure of oil in the ground, of obtaining it at no operating cost, and the apparently high income return hold a combined appeal which almost overshadows the less discernible fact that a very substantial portion, and very often all, of the income payment to this purchaser is a return of capital and that before he receives a return of his money the well yields may have approached the vanishing point. It is very difficult to convince the amateur that all oil wells are not profitable wells, even when they produce oil, and that there is a ceiling to the values relating to such properties.

Well-selected and fairly priced oil royalties are splendid investments, but they are in demand and are eagerly sought by experienced buyers who are amply fortified with knowledge and with cash to purchase those royalties which they consider to be in the class having prospects for future profits. Too often the royalties which reach the small and uninformed buyer have no such quality.

Royalties take many forms, and these forms may vary in the three chief items — the oil, gas, and casinghead gas (with its gasoline content). The *landowner's royalty* is the original form — the rental portion of the oil and gas retained by the original lessor, the landowner. If the lease is terminated, the landowner's royalty becomes equivalent to a mineral interest if it has not been limited in time.

The *overriding royalty* is an additional royalty taken out of the oil and gas produced, thus reducing the portion credited to the working interest. It is apart from that which the landowner receives, and usually arises from some transaction involving the lease. An oil company which desires the lease may compensate the lease broker for procuring the lease from the landowner, with an override. Or a dealer may add the royalty to the lease in assigning it to a buyer. A common form taken by a transaction of this kind results in stepping up the royalty rate from one-eighth to one-sixth; the original lessee, having taken the lease on a one-eighth basis (0.125), assigns it to the new owner at one-sixth (0.166⅔), the difference (0.041⅔) being the over-riding royalty. An assignment of this kind runs with the lease; when the lease terminates, so does this royalty.

A *participating royalty* is a misnomer because it does share in the expense of obtaining the oil. It is a synthetic term which has grown out of the class of transactions where some one acquires a percentage interest in the output of a certain well in return for the payment of a certain sum toward the cost of drilling the well together with an agreed fixed monthly contribution toward its maintenance and operation.

The expression is misleading to the extent that introduction of the word royalty implies no charges against the income. The interest is more nearly a form of working interest, where the participant who has taken an interest in the drilling of one or more wells has chosen to limit his liability. Thus, in return for a 10 per cent interest in the production from a certain well, he agrees that he will pay $10,000 on the completion of the well and $35 per month thereafter toward its maintenance and upkeep. The promoter, having sold enough of such interests to pay for the well, lets a turnkey contract and collects from his subscribers when the well is completed.

This type of transaction is often a very profitable one, especially with those wells which provide a flush initial production. After the well has matured and the cream is gone, it is more likely to be offered for sale, and it requires close scrutiny by the appraiser. The monthly cost contribution for operations continues in a straight line, while the productivity curve declines and the tax item, which has generally been overlooked or neglected at the time of the organization, becomes an increasing and inescapable drain on earnings.

Term royalty is a royalty anticipation or reservation which runs only for a definite period of years. Its advantage to the farmer is that upon expiration it leaves no cloud upon his title.

Minimum royalty is the lowest rate payable under the terms of a lease where the rate is variable and is derived from such factors as production rate, quality and price of oil, profits, etc.

Additional royalty is the increased royalty over and above the minimum royalty.

The *barrel royalty* is a unique form of royalty interest in the form of an assignment from the owner of a royalty portion of oil produced from a property, not of a fractional part of his royalty share but of one or more barrels per day (or thirty barrels or more per month) from the portion of oil that has been credited to him. The purchaser of a barrel royalty receives the first barrel each day out of that interest held by the seller; and, when the seller's interest has declined to a single barrel daily, the buyer gets it all. The occasion for this type of transaction arises when a seller expects the production rate to increase, possibly from the discovery of deeper sands or of increased allowables, etc.

Offset or *compensating royalty* is less tangible than the other forms of royalty and is really not a royalty; it is a payment by the owner of a lease to his lessor to whom he is under obligation to drill an offset well. The lessor agrees to accept, in lieu of requiring a well to be drilled, a royalty equal to all or a portion of the amount which he would receive if such a well were drilled and equal in yield to the competitive well.

LAND DESCRIPTIONS

Fortunately the United States General Land Office system of public-land surveys is followed in most of the states which provide oil production. The largest unit of area is the township, divided in 36 sections, each 1 mile square and containing 640 acres. The position of each township is identified by reference to a principal north-south line, called a meridian, and to an east-west line, called a base. A range is a series of contiguous townships, running north and south. A row of these townships in an east-west direction is a tier, more often referred to as a township. Thus Section 10, Township 32 South, Range 24 East Mount Diablo base and meridian designates a specific 6-mile-square surveyed area, situated 32 rows south of the Mt. Diablo base line and 24 rows east of that meridian. This is contracted to Sec. 36, T. 32 S., R. 24 E. MDM; or locally by those occupied in the Midway oil field to Sec. 36–32/24.

In some states where the division of land preceded the present system of surveys and in parts of Texas (which as a state retained its public lands when it came into statehood), no uniformity of design has been followed.

In parts of western Texas the land unit is the league, a square block containing 25 labors. The labor is a square which contains 177 acres. A common spacing pattern is five wells to the labor, or 35.4 acres per well, and the wells are usually placed one at each of the four corners, with a 5-spot location at the center.

In the dominion government surveys of Canada the townships are also 6 miles square and their numbering begins at the international boundary line and goes from south to north. Ranges are numbered west from 6 principal meridians, which are given numbers instead of names as in the United States. The range number precedes the meridian number; 3W4 means the 3d range west of the 4th meridian.

The Canadian township is also divided into 36 sections, but numbered differently from the United States. Subdivisions of the section are divided into 16 legal units, each unit representing a specific 40-acre tract similarly situated in each section.

LISTS AND DESCRIPTIONS

After the preliminaries as to point of view, purpose, date, etc., have been concluded, the initial step in a valuation is a list and description of the property which is to be appraised. There must be a clear account of what is included in the assets; and although it may be true that the appraiser understands fully the nature and the contents of the property, that is not enough. There should be sufficient detail so that misunderstandings and misinterpretations are avoided.

The description serves several purposes. It is a small matter to prepare a description when a single small property is to be examined. But when the property account comprises a considerable number of units, and the appraiser is not already familiar with them, the arranging and classifying of a list is the first step toward perspective on the extent and character of the job. A bewildering confusion usually surrounds the beginning of an undertaking of this kind, especially if the properties are widely scattered over a number of states and districts. During the compilation of the lists and descriptions, some orderly planning emerges from a perception of the scope and the needs of the work.

A final report will take a form which includes only a part of the data and information required in the course of an appraisal. For use as a basic control and work sheet when the property list covers a considerable number of tracts, it is convenient to use large sheets so that many of the data regarding each unit will be in one place. Then, as further classes of information are obtained and recorded concerning each unit, other columns on the sheet will carry additional material, obviating a need for again listing the names of each of the properties. All or a considerable part of the data regarding each tract is thus gathered together in one place. These sheets are extended by the addition of other sheets, sometimes until they become large and cumbersome, but they are the best means of assembling, comparing, and checking data and are a very convenient reference source.

A card record is also useful, especially if an appraisal is to be repeated. The cards, one for each property (Fig. 1), should be on paper which is stiff and strong enough to withstand use and much handling.

While an effort will be made here to cite all those items of data which at some time or other may be pertinent to an appraisal, it is not suggested that all are necessary in every appraisal. Useless information should be avoided; and, in these days when a multitude of outside examiners and checkers is visiting offices of oil companies in a never-

Operating Company: _____

Gr. of Oil: _____ Lease Name: _____ Field: _____

Price of Oil: _____ Description: _____ County: _____

Yield gas / bbl oil: _____ _____ Royalty Rate: _____

Yield gaso / bbl oil: _____ _____ Working Int: _____

Total yield / bbl oil: _____ Acres: _____ Co. Net Int: _____

Tax per bbl: _____ No. Wells: _____

Net per bbl _____

RECORD PAST PRODUCTION

Year	No. Wells	Bbls Oil	Bbls Water	% Cut	Gr	Depth of Pump	Cu. Ft. Gas	G : 0	Csg. Press.	Tubg Press.	Dys On	Method

Fig. 1. Arrangement of property records.

ending stream, it is strongly urged that the appraiser (1) limit his demands to essentials and (2) try to adapt his needs to the forms in which the data are set up in the company records. The direct and most comfortable course for the appraiser is to present the company with a form or tabulation, indicating specifically how the information required is to be compiled and arranged. But very often such a tabulation does not conform in any sense to the manner in which the data are arranged in the company records. A little preliminary discussion and inquiry, patience, and consideration may bring out a procedure which supplies the appraiser's needs, and at a greatly reduced effort on the part of the clerical force.

Titles and *ownerships* are not the concern of the appraiser. He assumes no responsibility for them; but it is in order for him to relate to his client any facts or observations which are pertinent and the extent to which he has taken them into account in his valuation.

Maps are desirable and are often essential, especially for showing the positions of developments on and near producing tracts as well as the position of unproved tracts with respect to nearby developments. They should be accompanied by a sufficient explanation in the text and should be the same size as the sheets in the report. Folding should be avoided if possible, and this can usually be arranged now that facilities for reproduction and reduction to any size are so widely available.

Unproved acreage requires less data during the course of an appraisal than is needed when the property is to be drilled, and much of the information is usually omitted from the final report when the lease roll contains a large number of units.

Data for Listing Unproved Acreage

> State and district
> Lease number and name
> Legal description
> Expiration date
> Gross acres
> Interest
> Net acres
> Rental
> Royalty rate, if other than 12½ per cent
> Notes as to unusual terms, contingent payments, etc.
> Unpaid cash balance due to lessor

In addition, if a single tract or group of tracts is being described, the account may well extend to the geographical situation, nearest town, transportation, nature of the surface, suitability for oil operations, the depository for rentals. When the tracts are not designated by lease numbers, the descriptions, names, and references should be particularly specific. The price paid for the lease, unless very recently acquired, is of no significance in a valuation. It does have meaning in an examination of the conduct of a company operation.

Oil companies that have a considerable collection of property units designate each unit with a number and identify each with the name of the landowner. When a long list is in preparation, the use of the name and number permits elimination of the legal description. The legal description is the most laborious and exacting portion of a property record and serves no useful purpose to the appraiser when he has access to maps which display the tracts and their situations.

Gross acres is the entire area of a tract, and if the whole lessee interest is held it is identical with the net acres.

DECIMAL EQUIVALENTS OF THE PRODUCTS OF FRACTIONS

0	1	1/16	1/8	1/6	3/16	1/4	5/16	3/8	7/16	1/2	9/16	5/8	11/16	3/4	13/16	5/6	7/8	15/16	1
1/16	0.0625	0.0039	0.0078	0.0104	0.0117	0.0156	0.0195	0.0234	0.0273	0.0313	0.0352	0.0391	0.0430	0.0469	0.0508	0.0521	0.0547	0.0586	0.0625
1/8	0.1250	0.0078	0.0156	0.0208	0.0234	0.0313	0.0391	0.0469	0.0547	0.0625	0.0703	0.0781	0.0859	0.0938	0.1016	0.1042	0.1094	0.1172	0.1250
3/16	0.1875	0.0117	0.0234	0.0312	0.0352	0.0469	0.0586	0.0703	0.0820	0.0938	0.1055	0.1172	0.1289	0.1406	0.1523	0.1563	0.1641	0.1758	0.1875
1/4	0.2500	0.0156	0.0313	0.0417	0.0469	0.0625	0.0781	0.0937	0.1093	0.1250	0.1406	0.1562	0.1719	0.1875	0.2031	0.2083	0.2187	0.2344	0.2500
5/16	0.3125	0.0195	0.0391	0.0521	0.0586	0.0781	0.0977	0.1172	0.1367	0.1562	0.1758	0.1953	0.2148	0.2344	0.2539	0.2604	0.2734	0.2930	0.3125
3/8	0.3750	0.0234	0.0469	0.0625	0.0703	0.0937	0.1172	0.1406	0.1641	0.1875	0.2109	0.2344	0.2578	0.2813	0.3047	0.3125	0.3281	0.3516	0.3750
7/16	0.4375	0.0273	0.0547	0.0729	0.0820	0.1093	0.1367	0.1641	0.1914	0.2188	0.2461	0.2734	0.3008	0.3281	0.3555	0.3646	0.3828	0.4102	0.4375
1/2	0.5000	0.0313	0.0625	0.0833	0.0938	0.1250	0.1562	0.1875	0.2188	0.2500	0.2813	0.3125	0.3438	0.3750	0.4063	0.4167	0.4375	0.4688	0.5000
9/16	0.5625	0.0352	0.0703	0.0937	0.1055	0.1406	0.1758	0.2109	0.2461	0.2813	0.3164	0.3516	0.3867	0.4219	0.4570	0.4688	0.4922	0.5273	0.5625
5/8	0.6250	0.0391	0.0781	0.1042	0.1172	0.1562	0.1953	0.2344	0.2734	0.3125	0.3516	0.3906	0.4297	0.4688	0.5078	0.5208	0.5469	0.5859	0.6250
11/16	0.6875	0.0430	0.0859	0.1146	0.1289	0.1719	0.2148	0.2578	0.3008	0.3438	0.3867	0.4297	0.4727	0.5156	0.5586	0.5729	0.6016	0.6445	0.6875
3/4	0.7500	0.0469	0.0938	0.1250	0.1406	0.1875	0.2344	0.2813	0.3281	0.3750	0.4219	0.4688	0.5156	0.5625	0.6094	0.6250	0.6563	0.7031	0.7500
13/16	0.8125	0.0508	0.1016	0.1354	0.1523	0.2031	0.2539	0.3047	0.3555	0.4063	0.4570	0.5078	0.5586	0.6094	0.6601	0.6771	0.7109	0.7617	0.8125
7/8	0.8750	0.0547	0.1094	0.1458	0.1641	0.2187	0.2734	0.3281	0.3828	0.4375	0.4922	0.5469	0.6016	0.6563	0.7109	0.7292	0.7656	0.8203	0.8750
15/16	0.9375	0.0586	0.1172	0.1562	0.1758	0.2344	0.2930	0.3516	0.4102	0.4688	0.5273	0.5859	0.6445	0.7031	0.7617	0.7812	0.8203	0.8789	0.9375
1	1.0000	0.0625	0.1250	0.1667	0.1875	0.2500	0.3125	0.3750	0.4375	0.5000	0.5625	0.6250	0.6875	0.7500	0.8125	0.8333	0.8750	0.9375	1.0000

Interest records the proportional ownership in property held jointly with others. The list, being a statement of the lessee or working-interest portion, usually ignores the royalty and indicates the proportion of expenses and of the lessee oil that is assigned to this owner.

Data for Listing Proved Properties

State or division
Number and name
County or field
Legal description
Acres — proved $\begin{cases} \text{developed} \\ \text{undeveloped} \end{cases}$
      untested
      condemned
Wells — producing
      drilling
      idle
      abandoned
      gas
      dry
Royalty rate
Company interest — in gross oil
                in working interest
Gravity range
Gravity average
Current price received (per barrel) — for oil $
                           for gas
                           for gasoline_____
        Total income per barrel of oil $
Current gas sales — mcf per month
Rate per mcf
Current operating costs
Average monthly overhead costs
Contingent payments due
Purchaser — of oil
Terms of contract
Purchaser — of gas
Terms of contract
Unusual lease terms

      Monthly or annual production to date, by lease or wells

Net acres represents the interest in the tract, expressed in acres. Thus, if a one-fourth interest is held in the leasehold on an **80**-acre farm, the net interest is **20** acres.

Notes regarding unusual features are seldom necessary because most leases follow a standardized pattern and differ in so small a degree that the variations do not have any effect on cheap and moderate-valued leasehold acreage. Any deviations of the royalty rate from one-eighth should be noted. Occasionally a payment out of oil is encountered, an unpaid balance due for the account of the purchase of the lease, some unusual development requirement, and at rare intervals some genuinely odd provision. During the early oil days many of the wells were named after ladies; occasionally a lease is found to carry on the tradition, with a provision that one well, when drilled, shall be known by some given name instead of by a number.

A simple form for assembling portions of these data is in Fig. **2**.

Company   Andor Oil Company

State Kansas		County Cowley					Field Haswell	
Lease		Wells					Interest in	
Number	Name	Producing	Idle	Abandoned	Dry	Gas	Gross oil	Working interest
224	Ralph	4			2		0.875	All
278	Armstrong	2					0.4375	$\frac{1}{2}$
279	Pyle	2		2			0.4375	$\frac{1}{2}$
292	Hoots	7			1		0.875	All
312	Porter	6					0.875	All
313	Law	4	2	2			0.218$\frac{3}{4}$	$\frac{1}{4}$
314	Leabow	2	2	4	1			

Fig. 2.   Arrangement of well data.

The extent to which the *plant facilities* and *equipment* at a property should be enumerated is a matter for decision in each situation. Certainly the major items of consequence should be noted and described, such as tankage, boilers and power equipment, buildings, gasoline plants, gas-compressor plants, etc. An inventory of all the items of machinery to be found on an operating property is a staggering task and contributes little more to a valuation than does a general account of the facilities, together with some detail about casing logs, the well-completion records, the methods of handling the flowing wells and the pumping wells, and the general type and condition of the machinery. Some measure of estimate is appropriate to the need and probable outlay for repairs and for additions incident to changing wells over from flowing to pumping, for dehydration, vacuum gas lines, etc.

DEFINITIONS

As often happens during the youthful period in an industry, the precise meanings of many words and expressions which have a wide use in the petroleum industry have not become clearly established, or have meanings that are not always uniform in different localities. H. F. Porter has endeavored to clarify the definitions in his informative *Petroleum Dictionary*, but this will not reform the vernacular of the oil fields, and it seems desirable to explain in somewhat greater detail the scope of meanings of some terms which are used in various ways and to point out the need for great care to guard against misunderstandings which might result.

Natural gas is a gaseous form of petroleum. Any gas found ready formed in nature is natural gas. But a custom has grown, in connection with the differentiation between (1) the gas which occurs along with the oil from oil wells and (2) the so-called dry gas which occurs alone and not along with oil, of calling the latter *natural gas,* and this expression has found a wide use in contracts and legal papers. This dry gas is also called *rock gas.* On the other hand, dry gas and residue gas are both terms which have been applied to that gas which has been treated and had removed from it the gasoline vapors it contained.

Production is a word which early enters any discussion of an oil property. The most frequent form is, "What is the daily production?" This inquiry obviously asks the amount of oil currently being brought to the surface. But in some statutes and administrative regulations, *production* refers to the capacity of a well or a property, the amount of oil or gas that the well is capable of producing. This amount the oil-field operator would call *potential.*

Potential production is the entire or the maximum amount of oil which a well can be made to yield during a specific time interval. The confusion and the variations in the use of the term grow out of the different time factors and operating conditions of a well in connection with the recording of its yield. A well flowing out of control may produce many times the amount of oil which it would be permitted to produce when handled to the best advantage as regards gas conservation and preservation of reservoir energy.

Potential does not always mean maximum capacity of a well because well capacities often increase for a time after they are brought in. Potentials are nearly always reported to be higher than they really are, where questions of curtailment are involved. On the other hand, the tendency is toward misleading reports on the low side when the initially and the subsequently reported potentials enter into the equation used by assessors for computing mineral land taxes.

When the test of a well potential is conducted under some controlled conditions which tend to provide a rate different from that of free and continued open flow, the result is *rated potential*. It can be made to read either high or low.

If the potential test is carried out in line with the provisions of some state regulatory body, the result is an *official potential*, one of the factors from which is derived the *allowable production* for each well on a property.

Settled production is an expression which has many interpretations. It is applied to the yield of a well or of a property. To the layman it can be seriously misleading if he accepts it to mean a productivity rate which has ceased to change or a decline that has come to rest. No experienced oil man would accept this meaning, but many ideas are held about the precise conditions which pertain when the term is used.

In the industry the term denotes some age and consistency of behavior after the flush period. It may designate the productive rate of a well thirty days after completion or six months after completion. On many occasions it has been used to mean that the productive rate has dropped to a level where the continued decline is moderate and fairly uniform. This corresponds roughly to the "flattened-out" phase of a curve of ordinary decline and, in general, to the period when gas expansion within the oil reservoir has ceased to play a principal part in bringing the oil to the well.

The Signal Hill field average production may be considered to be settled. The wells are nearly 20 years old, their average decline rate is 1 per cent per month. Recent Illinois wells were called settled when they were 8 months old and their average decline was 15 per cent per month. It is entirely a relative matter, and much of the significance of the term rests on who is using it and under what circumstances.

Gross oil production is the entire amount of clean, marketable (pipeline) oil produced from a property. It comprises all the oil, whether belonging to partnership interests, royalty holdings, or other distributed interests. In some regions, notably California, the expression as used in the oil fields is applied erroneously to the entire liquid from the well (oil, water, and emulsion) before the emulsion has been broken down and the water removed. For that reason, it is well when discussing the subject to question or to emphasize the meaning of the expression as used.

Net oil production is the amount of clean, marketable oil credited to any one interest. Thus, if a property is operated under a one-eighth royalty lease and it yields 100 barrels daily of clean oil, then the daily net production of the working interest, or operator, is 87.5 barrels. The use of the word net to describe the amount of clean oil, after dehydration and water removal and before deduction of royalty, is incorrect and misleading but is a common practice in California.

Productivity index is the daily production rate in barrels, divided by the pressure difference between the static or reservoir pressure and the bottom-hole pressure in the well when it is producing.

Oil reserves are discussed further in Chapter III. The expression is employed variously, the chief difference in meaning being a matter of economics. One school of thought holds that oil reserves embody only the proved oil which can be produced at a cost no greater than the price that the oil will bring. Another group places in reserves all the known oil, of whatever quality and wherever situated, whether or not its recovery would be profitable at today's prices. Still others refer to the *reserves* estimated to be in certain geological provinces, even though these oil bodies have not been found and are not definitely known to exist.

None of these indiscriminate uses of words can be said to be incorrect because there is no single authoritative guide and no established usage. For that reason, " recoverable oil " as a substitute has found favor with those who seek to suggest at least an implication of a test of commercial feasibility to known oil bodies before they are sanctified into a genuine acceptance as " reserves."

Unnecessary wells are often referred to, but in several connotations. Legally, the unnecessary well appears to be " any well which would fail to increase the ultimate recovery from the field by an amount sufficient to return the cost of investment, plus the cost of operation and royalties and a reasonable profit." A royalty owner considers the unnecessary well to be only that which is not absolutely requisite in the lease provisions. In some localities any inside location is called an unnecessary well.

Fee ownership is well accepted as meaning the full ownership of both the surface and the minerals. *Surface fee,* as its name suggests, is the title to the surface only. But, in some areas along the Gulf Coast, *fee* is also used to designate an ownership of the minerals (and, or not, the surface) under such terms that a perpetual royalty is outstanding as to oil and gas whenever they shall be produced, but without any expiration of the owner's exclusive right to develop and produce them and with no obligation on his part to do so or to pay rentals in lieu of drilling. Its superiority to a lease grows out of the fact that it does not terminate, does not require rentals or drilling. In these respects it has the advantages of complete ownership, and so has come to be called a *fee*. One who is unfamiliar with this local use of the term may conclude that the full mineral interest is being described, instead of a fractional portion which will bear all the cost of operations but is charged with an outstanding royalty.

Secondary recovery is used with various meanings to designate stages in the life of a well or a field. Although engineers are not in full agreement, the meaning they most generally apply to secondary recovery is oil obtained when the natural pressure differential ceases to be an agency in bringing the oil to the well. In business circles it is applied to those operations or methods which secure additional quantities of oil and gas from the reservoir, beyond the amounts obtained with the conventional methods. What is a thoroughly conventional practice today may have appeared to be unusual and bizarre a few years ago.

Lifting cost is an expression applied to mean either the entire field expense or only the actual cost of operating the producing wells. In the former meaning it covers the whole scope of activity and outlay, the outside development costs and central office charges, and is the concern of the field manager. In the latter sense, it embraces only the pumping charges of power, labor, cleaning out, and repairs, and is compiled in this form for the guidance of the local foremen and farm bosses.

REFERENCES

George H. Burrell, *The Recovery of Gasoline from Natural Gas,* 1925.

Wilbur F. Cloud, *Petroleum Production,* 1937.

Mid-Continent Oil and Gas Association, *Handbook on Unitization of Oil Pools,* 1930.

H. P. Porter, *Petroleum Dictionary,* 1936.

L. C. Uren, *Petroleum Production Engineering,* 1939.

CHAPTER III

UNPROVED LANDS

Over 3,000,000 acres of lands in the United States now produce oil or are proved to contain it. In addition, the lands which are unproved but considered to hold sufficient prospects to induce operators to lease them and to pay rentals for holding them total over 100,000,000 acres. Lands of this class comprise most of the holdings of an oil company. They are not producing and they contain very few tracts which ever will yield oil. The attention focused on them from time to time increases and declines with the two important cycles in the oil-producing business — the periods of over-production and of under-production.

The demand for crude oil seldom corresponds with the potential production rate. Nor can the future conditions as to discoveries of new oil fields be forecast. The search for oil and its production are functions of the geological conditions which govern its occurrence, and these continue to be vague and uncertain. Oil is a fluid. This fact, combined with the law of capture, has set up unusual competitive conditions surrounding its withdrawal. The result has taken the form of a series of alternating cycles in the relation of consumption or demand, on the one hand, to the production of crude or the discovery of new sources, on the other.

> 1. A period of over-production, when the output is greater than is required. Stocks of oil increase, the uses of its products become extended and spread out, through their ready utility and adaptability, in many directions; prices decline, accompanied by a decrease in new drilling and in the search for oil and for likely prospects.
>
> 2. A period of supply that fails to meet the demand. Then stocks are drawn on, increases in crude price schedules stimulate the development of undrilled productive areas, and the search for new oil and the acquisition of desirable acreage gets under way again.

We have seen that oil properties are divided into those which are proved and developed (producing) ; proved and undeveloped; and unproved. The second of these classes is of relatively small extent but is of great interest during the development and delineation of a new field and of great market value during cycle 2.

44

A favorite approach to the oil business by amateurs is to follow a period of study with an inquiry for some property containing producing wells, together with a considerable block of acreage that is proved but undrilled, and a group of carefully selected unproved tracts. Their objective is well chosen and evinces careful planning, for such a combination is perfection in the oil-production business. But usually the search is undertaken during cycle 2 and more often during the latter portion of it when oil properties are returning good profits, crude oil is in demand, and few properties are being offered for sale — at high prices by the oil producers who, as a group, comprise the world's greatest body of optimists.

Another division classes lands into (1) proved to be productive; (2) probably productive; (3) possible oil lands. This arrangement is a hangover from the mining conventions which came into use with ore deposits about 1900. It is of doubtful utility in the oil fields because definite limits cannot be set for distinctions between such descriptive terms. Ore deposits are much more tangible and more closely measurable than oil bodies. The classification is not only artificial but it also introduces danger of an error which can prove to be disastrous, of placing in oil reserves an estimated amount of oil which it is expected will be obtained from the " probable " or " semi-proved " acreage. The reasoning is simple. If in a district the average yield from the known productive land is 15,000 barrels per acre, and a given tract of probably proved land is considered to bear an even chance of becoming oil bearing, then it is held to qualify for 7,500 barrels per acre. Immoderate estimates of oil reserves and of property values result from this procedure.

A tract of land is either proved or it is not proved; and, if it is not proved, then no circumstance warrants crediting it with reserves. It is simply nonproducing and unproved acreage. It may have great value by reason of its prospects for oil, but it fails to qualify as proved land as long as a considerable doubt about proof remains. For appraisal purposes the only satisfactory index for measuring and recording its value is something corresponding to market value where, as of the specific time in question, the trading range of similar properties or of properties deemed to have similar prospects for oil is reflected.

It is a great advantage and comfort to the appraiser in a valuation of oil property holdings if they are found to cover a considerable number of units, with some geographic diversification. Then, if the yardsticks which have been adopted for application to the properties are reasonably correct and are carefully used, the law of averages will bring a valuation to a point within a proper range. This is especially true if a substantial acreage of well-chosen nonproducing leaseholds is included with the producing properties. Most engineers have had the experience of finding that, by reason of over-estimates of reserves, or of price, or of other factors, their valuation of a group of oil-producing properties has not conformed to the realized earnings; and yet the valuation as a whole has worked out because some of the former nonproducing acreage of low value were brought into the highly productive class.

MEASURES OF VALUE

No satisfactory workable formulas for the determination of land values of unproved prospective oil lands have been developed. Lands which are situated in the vicinity of a new and important oil-field discovery change in value swiftly as long as acquisitions are sought by earnestly competitive buyers. If they are situated farther from the scenes of activity, their progress in value is imperceptible as they come gradually to take on interest and promise for oil production. The demand on the part of lessees and the willingness of landowners to lease are the principal controlling influences, and these persons are guided by no established rules.

Lands which, by reason of geological conditions and evidence are universally accepted as having no prospects for oil, are obviously without value, notwithstanding that there may have been transactions in the oil rights. Much other land is situated so that its prospects for oil are not entirely negative although at the moment it does not engage the attention of the oil fraternity. It is the transformation of a small portion of such areas into producing oil fields that provides the new sources of supply for the constantly shifting centers of activity. In the course of this change the oil values of nonproducing lands are advanced from a nominal lease rate of $0.25 per acre to amounts of $1,000 or more or less per acre. Following this upward swing, as the proved productive area becomes delineated and outlined, that portion of the acreage which is definitely found to be nonproductive, and therefore valueless, ceases to engage further interest and attention.

Many influences come into play during the course of this cycle, and they are too intangible to lend themselves to a mathematical formula for measuring such values. Attempts in this direction have been confusing and misleading and account for some of the occasions when extensive purchases of oil leases have been carried out at price levels markedly out of line with the prices commonly paid by other buyers for acreage considered to hold equivalent prospects for oil.

The companies with consistently successful records of profits from the widespread acquisition of these lands of uncertain quality are those which have adhered fairly closely to certain general levels of prices for certain grades of acreage. The price guides which they have followed have been based on an indefinable background of experience that cannot be outlined by concrete reasoning but finds its justification in the fact that this type of company enjoys a continued success based on its wisdom and experience. Departures from the indicated price levels characterize either the concerns which try to buy at lower prices (and end with either no acquisitions or with the less desirable selections) or those which pay prices out of line on the high side (and end with the inevitable failure which results from paying more for properties than they are fairly worth). Merchants have a saying that " well bought is half sold "; this finds an appropriate analogy in the business of building up oil reserves through the purchase of unproved lands.

Of course the foregoing has many exceptions in the oil business. An occasional operator invests unwisely, or at unwise prices, for lands which later become highly productive. He then ceases to be an oil operator and is an oil producer; but his particular luck and experience have not altered the fact that the percentage is against the buyer who maintains continued high prices. A very small percentage of the lands leased for oil ever proves to be productive, and these lands must carry the load of the expenditures for those tracts which never produce.

Two features in the appraisal of unproved lands when " going prices " are a guide may be appropriately considered to provide some increment to the value of a group of unproved tracts to a company as a going concern. The first feature is that the value to a company of any specific tract comprises not only the buy-and-sell value as reflected in current prices but also those actual expenses which, quite apart from that figure, are necessitated in the acquisition, the escrow charges, the title examination, and other costs incident to placing the tract in the company land department files. This item may be only a few cents per acre for large blocks of cheap lands or it may involve a considerable expense for some small tract.

The second feature of property values when considered from the point of view of their worth to the holder as a going concern is some rather vague, but nevertheless real, value which exists in the ownership of a considerable number of well-chosen and well-distributed unproved tracts. The cumulative value of them, all taken as a group or entity, is genuinely greater than the sum of the individual units. The oil man refers to this feature as the " percentage" — a term which expresses the fact that in such a spread of leases nearly all will prove to be unproductive and valueless — but his experience has shown that a sufficient number of the total will provide production with which to make the venture profitable. The percentage rarely fails where the management is reasonably able and honest and where the operations are great enough in scope for the law of averages to prevail.

The problem, then, in approaching the valuation of many scattered properties in one ownership is to determine a proper yardstick of value to be applied to the various classes of acreage. If the judgement in this regard is sound and if the amounts named for each unit are consistent, the final total will be not only that amount which the properties are fairly worth to the owner as a going concern but also an amount which will permit a reasonable profit in the course of time.

Possibly this latter element of prospective profit is an equivalent of the mysterious " going-concern " value or " good-will " value which is found in such high favor in utility-rate cases, and has been introduced occasionally into valuations of oil companies. Aside from a consideration like the one outlined above, it is difficult to find reasonable justification for going-concern value as a separate or distinct additional factor in the measure of oil property values.

The continued references to the buying and selling of unproved acreage cannot be avoided because these transactions in unproved lands set up the only workable index of value at any one time. Since geophysics has come into such widespread and successful use in the industry as a tool for finding new places to prospect for oil, a considerable change has been reflected in the land portfolios of the oil companies. They have become much more selective in their choice of tracts within the regions where studies have been made and less inclined to hold large numbers of scattered tracts situated on a vague and indefinite geological trend. They are more disposed to narrow their choice and are willing to pay for it. When they fail to obtain leases which fill their exacting requirements, they buy royalties. The lessened demand for scattered and unrelated acreage has caused the price to decline.

All unproved land values are affected by and in a broad sense are dependent on the price of oil, the demand, the trend in discoveries of new fields, and the general relationship of discoveries of new supplies of crude to the withdrawals. Other factors which affect chiefly the value at any given time of a certain tract are

The known geological conditions

The leasing activity and competitive bidding for lands in the neighborhood

Exploration activities in the locality

Lease terms as to period, rental rate, royalty rate, development provisions, and obligations

Further discussion of the relationship of these factors to land values is contained in the account of Fair Market Value in Chapter VI. Something equivalent to market value is, on most occasions, the proper and most practicable means of measuring and recording acreage value. But occasions do arise when a departure from this point of view is in order. The worth of some tract of land to a particular owner or to some buyer may be low because his geology is unfavorable or because he has enough land in the vicinity. On the other hand, he may rate it high as far as his price ideas are concerned because his competitors hold leases and he is unwilling to remain shut out or because of some emotional trend which cannot be explained.

It is often puzzling to try to account, by any other theory than mob psychology, for the waves of leasing campaigns which sweep along at times. But generally there is a reason, and that reason and the activities which it provokes affect values as well as prices. The start may be nothing more than the leasing of large cheap areas of granite and granodiorite exposures in the Wichita Mountains for the purpose of having an annual report contain many acres of land " under lease." The appraiser will encounter many sincere and honest points of view that react on land values and with which he is not in accord. He should not ignore them, even though eventually he gives them no weight. After all, many clever and successful oil operators have followed a rule of paying a premium for a cemetery lease, with a lease on the poor farm as good second choice, without knowing that the reason they have come into the money at a rate better than average has been their situation on untillable hilly knolls which are topographic expressions of subsurface structures.

THE LEASE

The great majority of oil leases run for a period of 5 years and as long thereafter as oil and gas are produced in paying quantities. If not producing at the end of 5 years and if not being drilled, they expire. They require annual rentals in lieu of drilling and payment to the landowner of one-eighth of the proceeds from the sale of oil and gas.

Low figures in the price range for such leases are from 10 to 25 cents per acre initial payments, with like amounts as annual rentals in lieu of drilling. During recent years the low in payments for large blocks of leases was in Illinois; 10-year leases for 10 cents per acre bonus, no rentals during the first 5 years, and 10 cents per acre per year during the second 5-year period.

Tracts of somewhat greater promise, or situated nearer to proved fields, bring $1.00 per acre bonus and $1.00 annual rental. Scattered acreage situated in a general and indefinitely wide trend in the oil-field country, where within a fairly wide range one piece is acceptable as another so that some freedom of choice is open, brings from $2.00 to $5.00 per acre. Bonus rates of $5.00 to $20.00 are not uncommon in districts which are in greater favor by reason of ascertained geological and geophysical examinations. These rates increase as the developments and evidence cause tracts to become more promising, and especially where little acreage remains open.

News that a test well is to be drilled causes the prices to advance. The top figures for unproved leases are reached in those areas where thick sands and big productivity yields are the rule; for such leases, unproved but with good geology, prices reach $200 and up per acre, with perhaps the royalty at one-sixth and maybe some additional sweetening in the form of a carried interest in the profits after the lease and development expenditures have paid out.

Annual rental rates do not vary as widely, and seldom exceed $1.00 per acre except in California. There the lease forms and terms have more individualism, and they more often depart from conventional practices, with rentals which reach to $5.00 and $10.00 per acre per month in the high range for acreage favorably exposed to an important drilling test.

The highest relative prices and values are those which prevail as to single and isolated well locations in promising areas, where a 2-acre piece or a 1-acre schoolhouse lot contains room for at least one well, provided the tract is found to be productive. The acre then ceases to have significance as a unit of measure because a well location is being dealt in. Single-location leases having promise but not yet proved can be worth $5,000, and increasingly more than that as the developments approach. Fully proved single-well locations have brought as much as $10,000 for a lease which carried a 40 per cent royalty reservation to the landowner — and have paid off handsomely to the lessee.

In addition, the nuisance position of the small schoolhouse lot is a powerful weapon in the hands of a selfish and unreasonable operator. Two wells drilled on it can create offset obligations which in turn bring on a cluster of surrounding wells, much greater in number than necessary for any economic recovery of the oil. The value of such a tract to the lessees holding the surrounding lands (the price which they can better afford to pay for it than to permit a multiple-well development) is entirely beyond the fair average value of similar lands in the locality. Either the nuisance price or the equivalent adverse damage effect must be taken into account when appraising lands which have these tiny lots as neighbors in unfriendly hands.

With lands which are very promising as to their prospects or have actually become proved to contain oil, the considerations in transactions go over more and more to a part cash and part payment out of oil as produced. Such trades are known as " rabbit trades " when they include this feature of paying the seller largely with his own oil, a form of deferred or instalment payment that is often desired by the seller.

SELECTION RIGHTS

The general adoption of geophysical methods in prospecting has been the inception for another form of land-lease holding. Companies are reluctant to undertake an extensive and costly exploration program over a large area unless they have some tie on the land if only for the short period necessary in a reconnaissance. The rights to select are in the form of a contract which accords to the holder the privilege of exploring the lands and of receiving an oil lease for such portions as he may select, at a price per acre, terms and conditions that have been originally agreed on and set out in the contract.

Rights usually cost 10 to 75 cents per acre, depending on the demand, situation, terms in the lease, and the compensation to be paid for the lease. Appraisal of these factors at a time when the exploration work is going on is difficult and uncertain when the information about the results of the exploration work is not available. If it has progressed to a point of definitely negative results and has been well conducted, then the rights are valueless. On the other hand, indications of desirable exploration areas and the right to lease such lands under a selection contract at a nominal figure take on a demand which carries prices to a range between $5.00 and $15.00 per acre for preferred selections.

TOPLEASES

A never-ceasing burden to the oil operator who has a considerable number of unproved leases is the lease which is approaching its expiration date and is situated in an area which has come to hold some promise for oil but not enough to warrant starting a well. The landowner refuses to extend or to renew the lease because he has already executed another lease to another lessee, the new lease to become effective upon expiration of the current lease.

The present lessee, then, either must drill and possibly get a dry hole or permit the lease to expire and possibly find later that he has parted with a valuable property. Situations of this type are encountered by the appraiser in any review of large land holdings. A lease which is approaching expiration and has no prospects which warrant a renewal is without value. If the lessee purposes negotiating for a renewal, his preferred position in the matter of dealing with the landowner is worth some nominal amount of $0.50 or $1.00 per acre. If a toplease is out and the present holder does not purpose initiating a test well before the expiration date, it has no value.

Topleasing is considered bad form and is frowned on in petroleum circles. Nevertheless it is done, especially under the heated leasing activities which prevail in promising and desirable new districts.

Salt Domes

In most untested and prospective areas the land values grade off from the most promising tracts down to those which are considered to be worthless. The salt-dome type of structure along the Gulf Coast is an important exception to this gradual change in lease values. Occurrence of oil along the flanks of piercement-type domes is exceedingly erratic and uncertain, and usually very profitable when found. Such a structure ordinarily does not become mature and productive until 12 to 20 dry holes have been drilled in it. The value of the lease covering an entire piercement-type dome, which has been well indicated by reliable geophysical surveys, is approximately $250,000. This amount can be increased when the surroundings and the outlook are better than average; it should be modified downward when the area is small and the characteristics of overhang, slopes of the edges, tilting of strata away from the salt, etc., are less favorable.

The values of small single tracts on an untested piercement salt dome are erratic. If a prospect for cap production is precluded, then they are worth still less; and much depends on whether or not some major land holder in the neighborhood, who has the resources and the urge to do so, is to carry out the bold exploration that is essential for the thorough testing of this very uncertain and spectacular type of oil occurrence.

Deep-seated salt domes resemble domal structures elsewhere as far as their relations to leasehold values are concerned. Generally they require deep drilling.

Prospects for Deeper Sands

The possibility in a producing property of the existence of deeper sands is a form of prospective oil land that has a very real value, because many oil fields are revived after long periods of declining production rates by such discoveries. In situations where these sands are suspected to lie below the developed sands, but are not definitely known to be there, the holding from a valuation standpoint is equivalent to an additional tract of unproved acreage which usually enjoys the very helpful advantage of being held against expiration and rentals by the production of the known sands. Occasionally, however, leases contain segregations of deep sand rights or require that within a certain time they must be discovered and identified if they are to be operated by the lessee who has the upper sand rights.

Very often at the time of an examination the tests which have already been carried out have established the absence of deeper productive sands or zones, or the known geological conditions may be such that this is apparent. On many occasions, however, sands both above and below that which is exploited in a field have been carelessly penetrated and not perceived during the haste and confusion of the early days.

ROYALTIES

Mineral interests and royalty interests in unproved lands have values, are traded in, and at prices which vary from time to time in much the same way as do leasehold values. Some companies of considerable size confine their interest and ownerships to these mineral and royalty interests. The form of ownership is important since a mineral interest (title to the subsurface minerals) may gain in value through the expiration of a lease that is outstanding, whereas a term royalty interest which shares only in that oil produced under the provisions of a certain lease becomes worthless upon the surrender or expiration of the lease.

A curious fallacy that is widely held is the belief that the lessee interest and the one-eighth royalty interest in a producing property are of equal value. This ratio fluctuates widely under different circumstances. Some lessee operations either lose money or barely break even, leaving the lessor as the only gainer. Other properties with very high yields and wide profit margins return a working-interest profit of five or six times that of the royalty, and even greater ratios when the casinghead gas and gasoline provision allocates an increased proportion of these products to the lessee.

The royalty acre seldom sells for less than $1.00. At a known structure in the Mid-Continent area which is to be tested, it is worth $40 to $70 per acre; similarly, situated in west Texas, it is $12 to $25. In California, with the same outlook, it will be dealt in at $4.00 to $8.00 an acre per cent, equivalent to $50 to $100 a royalty acre. Of course, the local circumstances control swings of considerable variations of these figures, which are indicative only of the general and comparative prices and values.   Nearness to the location of a probable test, the oil fraternity's opinion of the geology, the extent of a scramble for royalty interests (which, in turn, is influenced by the extent of the dealers' sales of these interests), the character of the operator who is to drill a test, all these react on the price.   Prices and values then decline and advance with the weakening or improving of the prospects as the well is drilled.   Once a successful test has been accomplished and a new field has come into being, then the royalty interests are measured by considerations of the probable oil recoveries and the ultimate returns and the timing of them, with increased emphasis also placed on the regard for the character and ability of the lessee.

CHAPTER IV
OIL AND GAS RESERVES

Estimates of the recoverable oil content of a producing property are early steps in most valuations. They are not an essential element in every valuation because some are founded on payout estimates or on investigations of market value which at times can be quite independent of any effort to measure closely the actual oil and gas believed to be underground. But generally the existence of oil reserves and of their availability is the foundation of producing-property values, and so they have come to be the unit of measurement most commonly referred to in the discussion of properties and of producing companies.

The reserves attributed to a company may be expressed not only in gross barrels but also in terms of barrels per share of stock or of barrels per dollar value of the stock, and these various points of view contribute to the perspective. Such considerations set out the contrasts in the prices at which stocks are traded; they permit comparisons of companies and situations, and supply a series of indices of the number of barrels of oil reserves considered to be equivalent to a dollar of traded stock. The ratio varies widely with different companies, reflecting those conditions which investors take into account as to the quality of crude oil owned, the state of development, the probable profits, the characteristics of the company as to management, dividend policies, etc.

The study of underground oil has been extensive. Voluminous literature is open to the student and in it he will find the subject fully treated. The broad and casual descriptions given here are not intended to provide a sufficient background with which to solve the many field problems encountered by the appraiser. The effort is rather to identify with a general description those important features of oil and gas reservoirs which affect well behaviors and to review some illustrations of the form they take.

DEFINITION

No universally accepted meaning for the term *oil reserves* has become established. When the expression is an important item in a

55

report, it is generally wise to describe the scope of the use therein. Those features which are most commonly accepted as narrowing its meaning are

Proved Oil — proved to a " high degree of probability "

Recoverable — that portion of the underground oil which can be withdrawn by using methods recognized in the technique of today. This is fairly equivalent to " recovery factor "

Commercially — producible profitably at today's prices and operating costs and conditions as regards salability, controlled production rate, etc.

Under this use of the term it would not be proper to include in estimates of oil reserves that oil which is known to be in a sand but is non-recoverable; or oil which has not been identified but is hoped for; or the great amounts of oil contained in those properties found in the possession of every large company, which are being wisely held for the future because the oil is known to be there even though the exploitation under current conditions is not commercially feasible; that is, not recoverable profitably at today's prices and costs.

Gas which cannot be sold or utilized profitably is not a reserve except to the extent that it comprises a necessary backlog of supply for an existing pipe line and distributing system.

Two properties adjoin and contain underground oil in identical amounts. The wells have been drilled in the first property; in the second they are as yet undrilled. The production rates are such that, now the wells are drilled, it pays to pump them although the drilling costs will not be returned. That oil which these wells will obtain is reserves. The oil under the undrilled property is not because as a new venture the wells should not be drilled.

The degree of proof is an open question because petroleum is unlike the ore bodies in mines and cannot be observed and measured in place. Proof, therefore, should be fairly convincing and firm, for otherwise the inclusion of those illusory and uncertain bodies of oil which may be in existence, but are not so surely established, causes the expression to lose meaning and force.

The determination of reserves is at best an estimate which in any situation depends on many circumstances. No inclusive rule or course of procedure can be laid down as applicable to more than a very limited field or class of oil occurrences. But it is in order to warn the appraiser again of one guide, and that is to avoid forms of conservatism which lead one away from correctness and accuracy. His function is to record the facts and his conclusions with as reasonable thoroughness and completeness as may be possible. It is for his employer to consider and to weigh the extent to which those conclusions should be modified in a course of action.

The range within which estimates of reserves fall is a wide one and is probably the most uncertain single variable in estimates of oil property values. Even where a property is fully developed and the operations have been conducted over a period of several years, so that the estimate is worked out under the most favorable auspices, the conclusion may yet be expected to deviate from the correct answer in a range of plus or minus 25 per cent.

During the early stages in the development of a new field the range of this percentage deviation is greater. The narrowing of that range and the search for the most effective means of development and operation are the objectives in those extensive inquiries now conducted into oil and gas reservoirs and their behavior under varying operating practices.

DEPLETION

An oil property is a wasting asset and every barrel taken from it reduces the amount of oil that remains, thus affecting its capital structure. An established accounting practice is to write off against the apparent cash earnings an appropriate amount with which to reflect this depletion of the reserves. This is an amount in addition to those amounts which are set aside to care for the depreciation, wear and tear of equipment, and the physical facilities related to the recovery of the oil.

The depletion rate is a simple factor computed by dividing the sum of (1) the cost of the property and (2) other amounts incurred in the development which are not being charged to depreciation or operating expense by (3) the net estimated oil reserves. The result is a " unit value " per barrel which, when multiplied by the number of barrels produced during a specified period, usually the year, provides the amount chargeable against earnings when computing the taxable income. Theoretically, then, by writing off the depletable costs on this basis the costs will be amortized at the exact instant when the last barrel is produced and the productive life of the property has expired.

As a practical matter, ideas about the remaining recoverable oil change with the additional information which time provides, and so it is customary to revise these statements of oil reserves annually and thus use new and corrected unit values after each revision. This method is *cost depletion*. It may be computed for each individual tract owned by a company or for all the tracts contained in each district; or else all the properties, wherever situated, may be lumped together and a single unit value ascertained and applied.

Income tax accounting procedure for federal tax returns, and for the returns in certain states, permits an alternative course which comprises writing off for depletion an amount, equal to 27½ per cent of the sales of oil and gas, but in no case more than 50 per cent of the net profits. This is *percentage* or *statutory depletion*. The circumstances under which many valuations are made are such that the effects of these accounting matters should be taken into account.

Generally, estimates of oil reserves that are made for the sole purpose of establishing depletion allowances are observed to be on the low side. A change downward in the 27½ per cent depletion rate seriously will affect some companies by increasing the taxable income and thereby impairing net profits. On occasion this feature invites attention and should be spelled out rather fully in the valuation report.

Occurrence of Oil and Gas

Oil and gas occupy the pore spaces between the individual grains or particles in sedimentary rocks. The amount of room which is available for the accumulation of these fluids depends on the unevenness in the pore spaces, the cementing material which fills a portion of the spaces, and the amounts of water which remain there.

Essential to the accumulation of these products is a trap, which will be in one of two general forms.

1. *Structural traps* are caused by structural deformation of sedimentaries, into anticlinal folding, faulting, etc.

2. *Stratigraphic traps* are not marked by deformation of the strata. They are sedimentaries which hold the oil and gas through thinning or lensing out or through a change in lithologic character.

Traps of the second class have provided about one-third of the past production of oil and will probably supply more than that proportion in the future. Either type requires a *cap* or *cap rock* of some impervious material which serves to prevent upward migration of the fluids.

Reservoir. Within the body of the sedimentary, known as the reservoir, the fluids are separated in accordance with their respective specific gravities. The water, being heavier, is below; above it is the oil, usually containing some gas in solution under pressure; above the oil may be a body of free gas, called the *gas cap*. The interrelationship of these fluids and their control during the exploitation of an oil field have a profound effect on the ultimate proportion of oil and gas recovered from the reservoir.

No matter what the form of the occurrence of the oil and gas, whether in lime, or sand or shale, and whether accompanied by water, by gas in varying ratios, or by neither, the only oil which is brought to the surface is that which gains access to the well. Movement of the oil and gas through the interstices between the particles of sand or through the voids in limestones requires force of some kind. This is *reservoir energy*. It may be the effect of gravity as at Glennpool and Burbank, or the expulsive force of expanding gas that prevails in most new fields during their flush stage; or it may be the drive of the subjacent water. The nature of the force and its control affect the total recovery of oil from the formation, and the rate or timing of the recovery influences the value of the property.

Water drive is present in nearly all reservoirs and exerts some influence, either little or big, in the effective reservoir energy. Often it is the sole propelling force that drives the oil toward the well. It is widely believed that when water drive is conducted under ideal conditions the most beneficial production practice results, with a maximum proportion of the oil obtained and at a minimum of expense. Ideal conditions which work toward this end are thought to consist in such a control of the withdrawal rate that a fairly uniform water pressure may be maintained and may bring out substantially all the oil that is obtained under flowing conditions. Included among fields where water drive is the principal agency are Eldorado and Augusta, Kansas; Tampico, Mexico; East Texas.

Gas is usually present along with the oil and in sufficient volume and pressure to cause its expulsive force to be a chief energy element. This gas occurs either in solution in the oil or above the oil in an accumulation of free gas. As an energy source it differs from water drive in that the amount of gas is limited and declines both in volume and in pressure as a removal of a portion of the oil and gas progresses. Thus its utility continues to decline and eventually ceases unless it is compressed and returned to the reservoir. At some point during the withdrawal of the oil and gas the decline in pressure permits an escape of the dissolved gases into the gas cap, causing this to extend areally and to drive some oil into a further migration or change in position.

Thus, in an oil reservoir the occurrence can be under

1. No pressure at all
2. The hydrostatic pressure of water only
3. Both hydrostatic pressure and that of gas
4. Gas pressure and no water

But most oil fields are predominantly of the gas-expansion type, with water drive nearly always present as a secondary and not-too-well-understood influence.

Reservoir Measurements.   Reservoir studies are carried out through a number of agencies.   Rock conditions and their content are observed from analyses of core samples taken during the drilling of the wells and from the electrical resistivity devices for comparing the physical characteristics of formations.   The behavior of the fluid content is indicated from data relating to bottom-hole pressures and temperatures and to the gas-oil ratios.

Since surface pressures cannot be correlated from well to well, the measurement of bottom-hole pressure has been adopted as a means of recording the original pressure condition of a reservoir and those pressure changes which accompany the withdrawal of the oil.   During the early life of a field they indicate the primary condition of the fluid body and the trend of the rate of decline.   Changes in the bottom-hole pressures registered against the cumulative production also suggest some indication of the extent to which gas expansion is the chief energy source, the part being played by water drive, and the ultimate amount of oil that may be sought.

The productive capacity of a well is rated to be a straight-line function of the difference between the pressure in the reservoir and the pressure at the point where the oil enters the well.   It is possible, therefore, to learn the rate of production equivalent to various sets of pressure differences and from this to determine well productivity curves under restricted flowing conditions.   Such data are also used in various proration computations; but their interpretation requires care and experience, and partial data lead very easily to erroneous and misleading conclusions regarding formation conditions.   It is probably true in most fields that the number of barrels obtained per pound of pressure drop really increases as the reservoir pressure diminishes.

When the pressure data are not fragmentary and inconclusive, they do show trends in the behavior of a reservoir, the effects of production practices, and hence some signs of ultimate yields.   This is especially true when the oil occurs, as it does occasionally, in the joints and fractured open spaces of shale bodies.

A high *gas-oil ratio* suggests either a dearth of oil in the formation or else some open hole or perforated pipe exposed against a section of gas cap. The one indicates a limited oil supply and the other a rapid dissipation of the gas reservoir energy if continued. An ideal condition is a ratio that is equivalent to the amount of gas dissolved in the oil in the reservoir at the reservoir pressure. Ratios ranging between 500 cubic feet and 1,500 cubic feet of gas per barrel of oil raised imply good average conditions, although a good rate is below rather than above 1,000 cubic feet. The Van Pool in eastern Texas, a splendid example of the results from well-organized unit operations, produces under a ratio which varies between 300 and 400 feet.

Much guesswork seems to attend the reports of ratios and for this reason it is unwise to draw conclusions too closely before verifying the dependability of the figures. New fields and new flush wells tend to have high ratios. The ratio in a new well which flows without restriction will increase normally during the early period of its flowing life, followed by a turn downward and a diminishing ratio.

It must not be assumed that under restricted flowing conditions the ratio is a constant, for changes in the rate of flow affect the ratios, either up or down and not in accordance with any known rule. The actual amount of gas necessary to raise a barrel of oil varies with the depth, the weight and viscosity of the oil, the tubing size and its internal condition, and other factors. A general idea of the amount is shown in Fig. 3, which, however, is not specific and is of interest chiefly for comparisons of relative amounts needed under varying depths and pressures.

Permeability, the readiness with which the oil and gas move through the interstices between the rock particles, is an important quantitative determination made possible by the coring of reservoir rocks. The tightness of sands was not measured in the early days of the industry, but the influence was recognized and glycerin introduced for the purpose of loosening the pay formation. By 1915 the young army of geologists employed the vague expression "sand conditions" as a sufficient if obscure explanation whenever wildcat wells failed to respond.

The permeability unit is the millidarcy. Anything below 25 would be considered a tight and uncommunicative sand. Good conditions are indicated by 200 or 300; 600 to 800 is in a high range. Limestones and dolomites because of their extreme permeability have been the reservoirs of most of the spectacular wells with the very great initial production rates. The permeability factor varies during the life of a reservoir, as does also the viscosity of the oil.

Porosity, the proportion of open space or voids in the rock, is not to be confused with permeability. The interrelation of porosity and

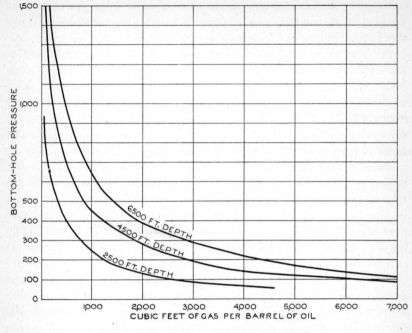

FIG. 3.   Gas volume required for lifting oil.

permeability is not too well understood, and certain generalities that one is a measurable function of the other have received some acceptance but have not appeared to be well warranted.

Connate water, or fossil water, is throughout the oil and gas reservoir. This is marine water which was trapped in the sediments and has remained there since they were laid down. It is saline and in the form of bottom water and edge water is readily recognized; moreover it is now known to occupy as high as 35 per cent or 40 per cent of the pore space of the reservoir.

ESTIMATES OF RECOVERABLE OIL

Any consideration of oil reserves as related to the value of a property takes into account (1) the actual volume of the estimated recoverable oil; (2) the timing of its being brought out. It is both difficult and often impossible to consider one without the other. When the wells have been drawn on for a sufficient time at their approximate capacity, the most trustworthy estimates of the remaining reserves are obtained from curves which record diagrammatically the past production rates and the extrapolation of them in a pattern of probable future annual recoveries. Until the restriction of production through the widespread application of curtailment and proration had become established, this was the method followed almost universally.

Oil reserves are much more uncertain and vague than are ore bodies, and efforts to measure their extent are more difficult and perplexing. Not only are they out of sight in a visual sense, but they are also actually fleeting. They have mobility. This fugitive character caused a Pennsylvania judge in 1875 to conceive the idea that oil and gas resemble wild animals. The problem before him was one for which he had no precedent, and so he wrote that notion into his decision. Other courts accepted and elaborated it, and thus it finally grew into the law of capture, which holds essentially that ownership of the oil and gas follows the act of reducing it to possession. It seems a far cry that the law should have invoked the legal principles of wild game and have applied them to the acquisition of subsurface oil and gas. The law has done nothing since then to remedy this obviously artificial paradox.

Two principal methods are usually relied on for estimating oil and gas reserves. The *volumetric* or *saturation method* ascertains facts about the size and porosity of the strata, their oil and gas content, and the part believed to be obtainable. The *decline-curve method* uses plotted records of wells which have been drilled on the property or in the locality, and from projections of these curves secures ideas of the remaining obtainable oil from the wells already drilled and from those to be drilled.

Volumetric Method. Carrl in 1878 defended porous sandstones as competent reservoir agencies, as against the contentions that large flowing wells must have their sources either in crevices or in a series of lakes or caverns. He had determined experimentally that samples of the Third Sand at Tidioute (the third Bradford sand) had an absorptive capacity of 7 to 10 per cent, without pressure, and from this and the known thickness of the sands he computed the district to have a producing capacity of 15,000 barrels per acre.

The volumetric method is essentially a study of the space in the oil-containing strata, the proportion of the pore space which contains oil and the proportion of that oil commercially recoverable. In the pore spaces of the oil-bearing formations are stored fluids in the forms of oil, water, and gas. The gas may be dissolved in the oil, or it may often be both in the oil as well as apart from the oil in the form of a gas cap. A portion of this mixture will be brought to the surface; there it will change in volume by reason of the temperature adjustments and the escape of the associated gas. The equation which expresses the volume of recoverable oil is of long standing.

$$\text{Barrels per acre} = A \times S \times P \times O \times R \times 7758$$

where A = area of proved tract in acres

        S = sand thickness in feet

        P = porosity expressed as a fraction of the sand volume

        O = space occupied by oil and dissolved gas (saturation factor), expressed as a fraction of the pore space

        R = percentage of oil that is recoverable (recovery factor), expressed as a fraction

    7758 = barrels of 42 gallons per acre-foot of volume.

The *area* may comprise an entire tract that is to be appraised, if it is proved to be fully productive, or only a limited portion may be indicated by the subsurface contours or by other evidence. Sometimes the division line is clearly marked, and at other times it cannot be clearly delineated and must be surmised, especially where the oil occurs in a thick sand with a tilted water table and the boundary of the interface between the oil and the edge water is a band of variable thickness.

Sand thickness is in some fields a very simple and uniform element. In others it is quite variable, so that here is meant the average thickness of that portion of the sand which contains oil rather than any portion situated above the interface between the oil and the superficial gas or gas cap. It is here that much of the former uncertainty regarding measurements has been clarified through the contributions of coring, core analysis, and electric logging.

Failure to recognize the important differences between sands which are oil saturated and those which are barren accounts for some of the early dogmatic statements regarding the small percentages of oil ultimately obtained and the consequent conclusions about " waste." It is now apparent that very substantial portions of the sands that were considered to be saturated have always been barren and never contained any oil; also that low permeabilities have formed an effective barrier against passage of oil to the well.

These differences were reflected in the easy and gradual steps taken by cable tool drillers when drilling in a well. After penetrating the sand for a short distance, they would cease drilling and observe how rapidly the oil rose in the well; then hitch on and run out another ten feet and let the well stand again, sometimes for several hours or overnight. In this manner was obtained a homely but reliable observation of the factors which are now designated saturation and permeability.

Behavior of the tools in the sand also indicated its character, and conclusions derived from all these signs were carefully drawn, even if seldom recorded. Fortunately, one trustworthy record remains for the appraiser in those areas where the wells were torpedoed. Glycerin has always been expensive, and farm bosses would shoot only those sections considered " good " sand. The shooting record is invariably a reliable index of the genuinely productive sand, rather than that which is recorded in the well log written in the diary of the supply company and found in the box attached to the headache post.

Porosity, either the open space between the particles of sand or the voids in limestones, is expressed as a percentage of the total formation volume. Uniformity of texture is not common, and porosity percentages vary widely.

Saturation factor is the percentage of pore space occupied by oil and its dissolved gases, expressed in terms of gas-free oil at normal temperature. The remaining space may contain either free gas or connate water.

Recovery factor is the proportion of the estimated underground oil that can profitably be brought to the surface. It and the connate water determination present the most perplexing questions in the use of the volumetric method. Many influences are integrated in the recovery factor, including permeability, the presence and behavior of edge water, the effects of the shape and nature of sand particles in causing adherence of a film of oil, and the *shrinkage factor* (relation of the volume of gas-free oil at the surface to the volume which it occupies underground, at higher temperatures and containing dissolved gas). The ultimate recovery is also affected by the rates at which the oil is removed. Excessive withdrawal rates cause a dissipation of gas and an uneven movement of edge water, which may flow rapidly along the more permeable portions of a sand and thus trap off the oil contained in the less permeable sand bodies or stringers.

The best evidence from studies of old fields which are either fully depleted or largely depleted indicates from the record of oil produced that the recovery factor has ranged from 15 per cent to 45 per cent for oil. For dry gas it is, of course, much greater.

Those old properties whose past production is fully known and whose future can be closely estimated provide the best evidence of yields of oil per unit volume of reservoir formation. It requires 7,758 barrels of 42 gallons to equal one acre-foot of volume. A porosity of 20 per cent provides room for 1,551 barrels of interstitial space. Yields from many run-of-the-mine properties range between 150 and 250 barrels of pipe-line oil per acre-foot of sand. Richer occurrences grade upward. Yields of 400 barrels, although not uncommon, are not the rule. For all practical purposes the high point is about 1,300 barrels per acre-foot, in the prolific Tertiary sand pools of the Gulf Coast and in a few areas in California. They are not the standard yields, but generally are found where all the conditions appear to be favorable.

Records of very high yields from single wells and from small properties, of which there are many, are exceptional performances caused by a much wider drainage area than is indicated by the property boundaries. This may be due to faulting or to unusual porosities and permeabilities which cause the oil to be drawn to the well from considerable distances.

Here again, the ascertained yield per acre-foot is closely related to the thickness of saturated sand, and the information on many old fields is fragmentary and uncertain. Assumptions of wider sands than actually exist are not confirmed by the screen and perforation records of old wells. The length of screen inserted in the well can be assumed to express the opinion of the maximum thickness of productive oil-saturated sand held at the time the well is completed. Records of perforating jobs on casing in place indicate the ideas held by the drilling crews or the engineers about the pay formations.

Additional Volumetric Factors. The *position on a structure* of a specific tract may lead to a considerable modification in a volumetric estimate when the situation has been examined with respect to a possible secondary gas-cap extension, or to the invasion of edge water under an assumption of either a homogeneous sand or one of varying permeabilities, or to a variety of operating practices conducted at the neighboring properties.

Wide spacing of wells ordinarily brings about another limitation in recovery. The productivity of the reservoir sand may be such that wide spacing is more profitable to the lessee than development on a more dense pattern of wells, even though substantially more oil might be obtained from the increased number of wells, and at an earlier period. Frequently, however, the economics do not control this feature because of the lease terms as to drilling requirements and to those obligations which result from irregular land shapes and the crowding of offsets. All these factors affect the actual number of wells drilled and in turn influence the recovery factor.

Illustrative of how the spacing pattern may change even after many years of production is the Healdton property shown in Fig. 4. The 38 wells followed an entirely conventional course until the year 1929, when pressure drive was applied to the sand and a small vacuum to the casingheads. This arrested the decline for a short time. Then, during 1935 and 1936, 22 additional wells were drilled (in this property which has been producing since 1915).

A *lime reservoir,* instead of sand, leads to estimates of oil recoveries that are less definite, especially during the early development of a field. The porosity is a controlling influence and this type of occurrence is characterized, in the absence of restrictions on production, by high

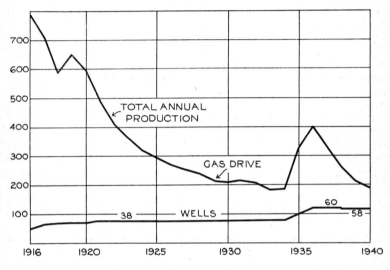

Fig. 4.   Production sustained by gas drive and additional drilling.

initial yields, rapid decline, and very often a dearth of gas.   Porosity is often found to be extremely variable within short distances, so that the recovery per acre may likewise lack uniformity.

Wortham, Texas, tells a story of unrestrained flush production and rapid exhaustion (Fig. 5).   It was discovered in 1924.   During the following single year it produced about 80 per cent of its entire ultimate yield of oil.   Recent interspace drilling is providing some small increases in production rates.

Volumetric estimates fail to provide anything more than generalities as to the *timing* and the rates of oil withdrawals.   On the other hand, the timing normally influences the estimates, because of the increased recovery factors which slow recovery rates may promote, through a better scouring of the oil sand and the elimination of the deterrent effects of variable permeabilities.

Another phase of the timing element is the demand for oil, a matter which can cause an entire cessation of operations.   An irregular history which reflects the market demand is that of the Dallas Derby (Fig. 6), Fremont County, Wyoming.   It was discovered in 1883, and

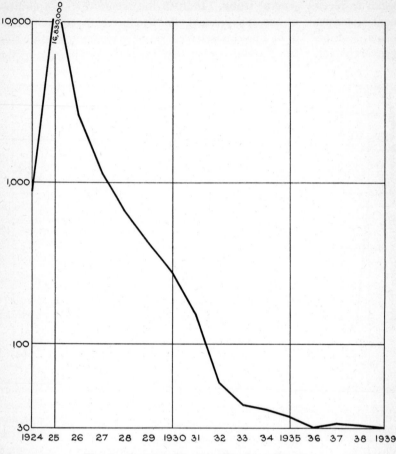

FIG. 5.   Rapid-decline rate (Wortham, Texas).

has changed hands several times.   The first oil was marketed in 1913, and the intermittent production since then has depended entirely on market outlets.

Decline-curve Method.   This method of estimating recoverable oil is applicable to wells or to properties whose development and history permit expressing diagrammatically the productive record of a well or of a group of wells.   When the wells have produced freely and without curtailment, the decline curves provide a basis for a forecast of the future through extension (extrapolation) of the curves.   Until the introduction of curtailment and proration this was the principal method used for such estimates.   The indications provided from restricted wells are less definite.

About 1910 this graphic representation of oil-well production records began to receive general study. In 1915 the report of the Appraisement Committee of the Independent Oil Producers' Agency of California described oil-well productivity curves as a means for estimating recoverable oil. The Revenue Act of 1918 led to the publication by the

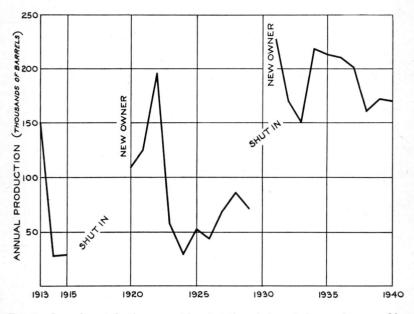

Fig. 6. Irregular production caused by shut-in periods and changes in ownership.

Bureau of Internal Revenue of the *Manual for the Oil and Gas Industry,* and this brought together much information from many sources concerning the subject and especially the adaptability of decline curves for that purpose. The expression " decline curve " has become too well established ever to be changed, although the curve is often found to increase rather than decline.

Curves which show the production records of wells that have flowed freely generally take a form similar to an hyperbola.

A typical curve is that in Fig. 7. The yield from the well during the early years was

Year	Barrels	Cumulative
1	38,000	38,000
2	21,200	59,200
3	13,300	72,500
4	9,100	81,600
5	6,600	88,200
6	5,040	93,240

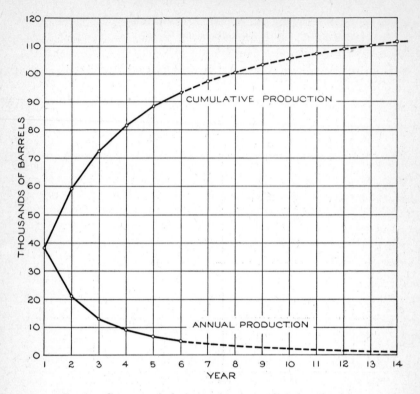

FIG. 7. Curves typical of annual and cumulative productions.

The *cumulative production* curve, also shown in Fig. 7, expresses the total production up to any specific time. The *ultimate production* is the total amount, either known or estimated, that the well produces during its life history. Curtailment of production rates has also deprived cumulative curves of much of their significance. Well performances when under severe and arbitrary restriction supply little help for estimating ultimate recoveries.

The well record can be plotted on logarithmic coordinate paper and shifted one way and another by trial until it assumes a shape that is either straight or very nearly so. The center line in Fig. 8 meets this requirement, whereas the lines to the right and left take the forms of curves even though they record the same data. A straight-line extension of the center line supplies an estimate of the future yields for ensuing years. This can then be plotted on rectangular coordinate paper, with a precision in the extrapolation that could not be attained except with the aid of the logarithmic plat.

Year	Barrels	Cumulative
7	4,000	97,240
8	3,200	100,440
9	2,620	103,060
10	2,200	105,260
11	1,860	107,120
12	1,610	108,730
13	1,400	110,130
14	1,240	111,370

It is also possible to plot the past production and a forecast of the future on semi-log paper, as in Fig. 9. The adoption of semi-log paper has not received universal approval chiefly because it does tend to-

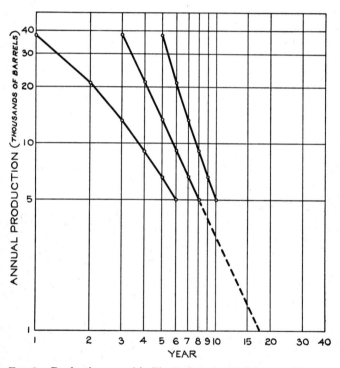

Fig. 8. Production record in Fig. 7 plotted on full-log coordinates.

ward underestimates. But some of the objections appear to be academic, and many appraisers feel that in experienced hands it is as reliable a guide as, and much more expeditious than, the cumbersome full-log curve. Whichever type of mathematical paper is employed, the technique is merely that of putting an equation into such graphical form that it can be extended with the use of a straight edge.

Sometimes it is desirable in practice that a curve for each separate well be prepared; but more often this cannot be done because the well records either are not available or are considered to be untrustworthy for the individual wells. Once an entire property is fully developed and has been producing over a moderate period, then the average gross

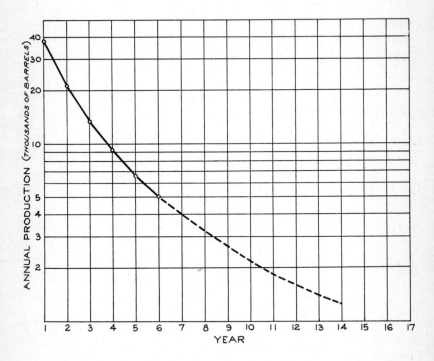

Fig. 9.   Production record in Fig. 7 plotted on semi-log coordinates.

production rate, quite irrespective of changes in the number of wells that are idle (provided they are not deliberately shut down), is in many ways the most useful form of picturing the behavior of the property. This curve integrates all factors such as repairs and re-drilling, seasonal effects, temporary shut-downs for various purposes, abandonments, etc., as may reasonably be expected to affect the property throughout the future just as they have in the past.

Figure 10 contains in the three forms of presentation an identical record of the annual well production from the first 44 Pliocene zone wells drilled at Dominguez, and operated prior to the introduction of proration and without any substantial restriction of flow. The individual wells varied in a considerable range, but the average of the group as an entirety suggests a consistent form and rate of decline.

Economic limit is the time point when the well no longer provides a profit. Since this is a function of such variables and intangibles as the yield rate, the price of oil, the operating costs, and the other factors which control profits, it is entirely a matter of estimate and it changes from time to time as the price of oil and the other factors change. Old settled properties produce over a much longer period than the estimates ordinarily acknowledge because, along with the diminution in profits, a greater effort is put into the reduction of costs.

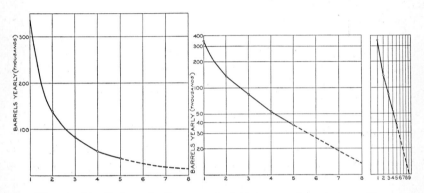

FIG. 10. An identical production record plotted on rectangular, semi-log, and full-log coordinates.

Estimates of the probable economic limit point for properties which contain more than one well are usually based on average conditions, both as to productivity and profits. As time goes by, however, the nearly exhausted wells that are money losers (the " boarders ") become eliminated, the materials and equipment from them are utilized for replacements at the remaining wells, and the property gains a longevity beyond what was indicated in a forecast based on averages. Notwithstanding that this feature tends to lengthen the life and to increase the amount of oil ultimately recovered from a property, it is not important as far as values are concerned because the present-day actual worth of the long-deferred earnings is slight.

The *family curve* is a composite compiled from the records of many wells in a single district. It is related to the so-called law of equal expectation, which holds, " If two wells under similar conditions pro-

duce equal amounts during any given year the amounts they will
produce thereafter, on the average, will be approximately equal, re-

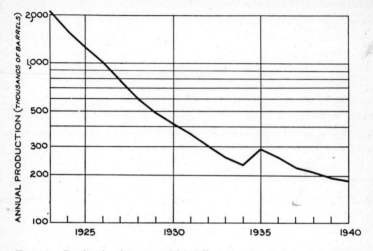

FIG. 11. Production increase which followed a change in management.

gardless of their relative ages." (*Manual for the Oil and Gas Industry*, page 88, 1920.)

Irregularities in Curves. The curves which represent average conditions and the average behavior of a large number of wells within a

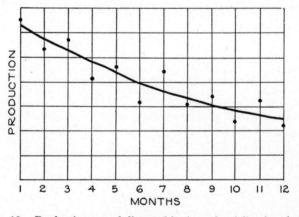

FIG. 12. Production record distorted by irregular deliveries of oil.

district are almost invariably uniform and smooth, especially in
reference to wells which have been operated at or near their maximum
capacity. But individual wells, or a group of wells under one control,

reflect the influences of production technique, crude prices, curtailment, and a variety of operating conditions which lead the curves to depart from conventional textbook form. Some of the causes are natural and unavoidable; others are man-made. Their study is an interesting pursuit, and the estimates of future yields cannot ignore the implications of these irregularities.

A change in management during 1934, at Cat Creek, was followed (Fig. 11) by a perceptible increase in production and a significant lessening in the rate of decline.

Minor ups and downs in the monthly figures may be caused by nothing more than the delivery of an additional tank of oil on alternate months (Fig. 12). This results from following the pipe-line ledger figures which are the sales and deliveries of oil, and not the well production. Many production records would be much less uniform were it not for the common practice among pumpers and gaugers of holding back a little oil in the reported gauges, to tide themselves over when the machinery breaks down, or when they sleep late, or just to avoid the bother of writing explanatory reports when minor mishaps have slowed down operations.

Small irregularities iron out when a long-range view is taken, as in the comparison afforded in Fig. 13. These irregularities relate to the production and the crude price variations of a Midway property which was fully drilled by 1911, and after thirty years has 55 producing wells remaining. The oil is heavy, has little gas, the productive measure is a thick sand body which has yielded thus far in excess of 50,000 barrels per acre. Wartime price increases in 1916 stimulated the production. In September, 1921, an oil workers' strike disturbed matters for a time. In 1929 the wells were shut down. Full production was not resumed until 1935, when the wells returned with substantially greater yields than when they were closed in. This experience is not uncommon.

In Fig. 13 the upper sketch shows the record of production by months. The lower part shows the same information expressed in annual production rates on semi-log coordinates. This supplies a more satisfactory trend delineation from which to estimate the future rates or the remaining oil.

Price conditions often upset theories of decline rates. Figure 14 is the record of a Kern River field property containing 75 wells. It was fully developed by 1911, and during the ensuing five or six years the decline took the appearance of a textbook curve. But the spectacular price increases which accompanied World War 1 began in 1916, and the incentive provided by $1.60 for 12° gravity crude set up an im-

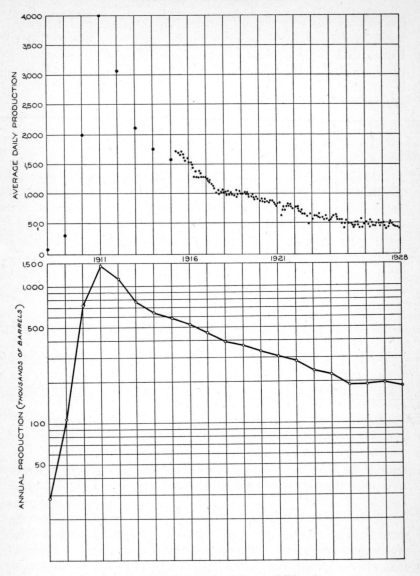

Fig. 13. Sustained production rate (Midway).

petus that quite reversed the curve. A reasonable forecast as of that time is indicated in the dotted line; the actual increase in productivity rate and amount of oil taken from the property was quite different.

During recent years this property has been operated continuously because of certain conditions in the lease agreement, but at times its

productivity has been curiously affected by the conduct of the neighboring operations, and in a manner quite contrary to accepted ideas.
During 1932–33–34, a period which included NRA days, the production
curve turned downward in spite of the fact that there was no cessation
in the effort to get oil from these wells. And this happened also in
spite of the fact that the neighbors were less energetic and shut down

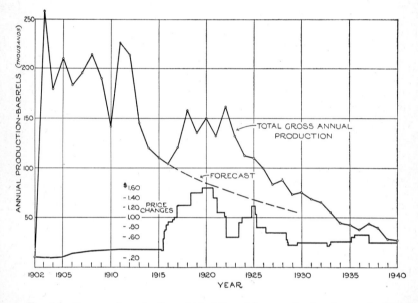

FIG. 14. Increased production which followed improved prices for crude oil
(Kern River).

their wells, notwithstanding the NRA ruling that they should continue operations. The neighbors simply drew from accumulated stor-
age the oil with which to supply the production and pipe-line runs
which were reported as currently produced — a neat reversal of the
more common practice of over-producing and under-reporting. The
result took the form of a heavier accumulation of water in the sand
than the pump capacity of the one operated property was able to
handle by itself. All the fluid which might reach the wells could not
be lifted; the water percentage accordingly increased and the oil production suffered.

During 1936–37 a general resumption of pumping in the district
relieved the water burden and benefited these wells, as appears in the
upward flicker in the curve in 1936. This takes a form not unlike
that of a well when it is changed over from flowing to pumping, at a

time when the productivity index has been greater than the actual well yield.

On the other hand, an entire shutdown of all the wells in a district may cause the reservoir conditions to become balanced or adjusted so that, when pumping is resumed, the yield rate assumes a higher position than was expected from an extension of the decline curve. The

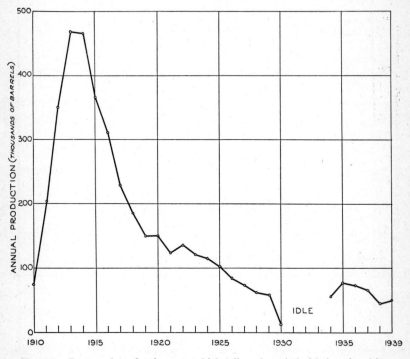

FIG. 15.   Increased production rate which followed period of being closed in.

production performance of a group of wells after the introduction of curtailment in 1930 appears in Fig. 15. These wells were completely shut down, and the allowable production " transferred " to properties of the company situated in other fields. Operations here began again in 1934. No genuine measures of well potentials have been taken, and no specific indications of decline rates are disclosed. The appraiser's best recourse here is to the field, in order to learn as much as he can about the behavior of the wells when pumping was resumed, the ratios of water, the height of fluid in the hole, the condition of the wells, the pumping-off periods and other indications of well capacities.

If a shutdown has been general so that a property has not suffered drainage to any material extent, the chances are that a normal projection of the curve as it appears at the time the wells were hung up will supply a sufficiently accurate measure of the remaining oil. But if the surrounding properties have continued in operation, then the problem is confusing. Drainage effects are very difficult to analyze

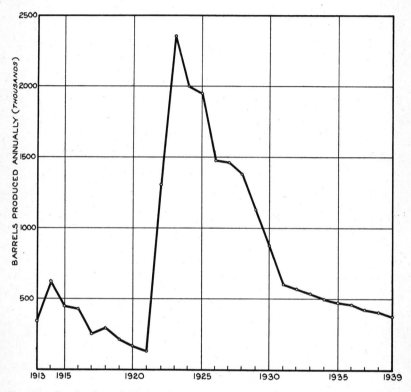

Fig. 16. Production which has been curtailed since 1929 and has conformed to umpire's allotments since 1931.

and to measure. Curtailment as an industry policy was first introduced seriously in the Mid-Continent region during the year 1925, and in 1928 was applied on a wider front. In California it became effective March 15, 1930.

The record of production from a typical property whose rate has conformed strictly to the umpire allowables is shown in Fig. 16. An increase in production followed the discovery of a deeper sand in 1921, and the development of this sand continued until 1926. The early portion of the curve, prior to 1929, pictures the full measure of the well capacities to produce; but pinching in has resulted in making uncertain any efforts to determine within reasonable limits the remaining amount of oil, because the withdrawal rates after 1930 conform to an artificial order and reflect only approximately the actual

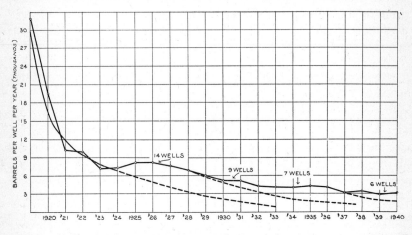

FIG. 17. Production better than forecasts that were based on past average well performances.

decline in capacity of the wells. It is certain that their total capacity is some amount in excess of the actual rate, and a projection of the

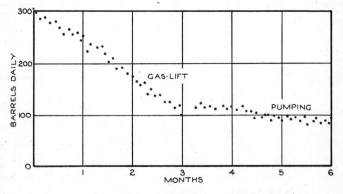

FIG. 18. Gas lift replaced with pumping (Seminole).

rate can best be described as merely a forecast of the estimated future umpire allowables.

Continued operation of a well in the flowing class is a false form of economy that was more common when less was known about gas-oil ratios, gas control, and the application of knowledge about productivity indices and proper tubing diameters. In Fig. 17 the production from a Stephens County property is shown, with the upturn in production rate in 1923–24 after placing the wells on the beam. The several erroneous forecasts of decline trends that are indicated here result from failure to take into account the probability that the average well production would not continue to decline because the better-than-average wells would survive the weak.

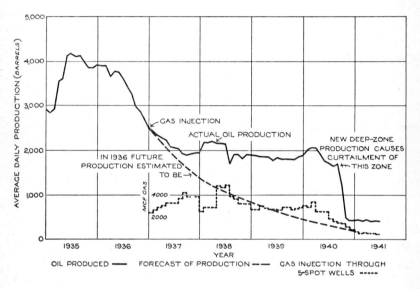

FIG. 19. Production rate sustained by gas injection.

The decline rate, in a well where gas lift was employed inefficiently, was arrested by replacing the gas lift with pumping. The record in Fig. 18 is that of a Seminole well.

Gas injection through selected 5-spot wells distributed over a property occasioned the history shown in Fig. 19. The development was completed early in 1936, and at the end of that year a forecast of the future might reasonably have been the forecast shown in the graph. But the introduction of gas into the sand and its recycling accomplished this departure from such a forecast. Late in 1940 a deeper sand was discovered and led to a severe curtailment of the older wells.

The characteristic steep-decline rates of Wilcox sand wells appear in Fig. 20, which shows also the benefits from gas drive applied at a time when these wells were approaching the economic limit.

Productivity rates are often affected by the completion of nearby wells in the same sand; this interference is especially apparent during

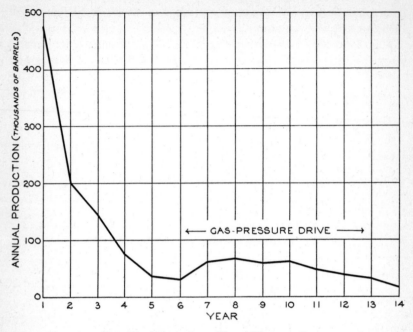

FIG. 20.   Effect of gas drive (Wilcox sand).

the early life of a field and in those areas where the permeability conditions promote a ready distribution of flow and pressure.   Figure 21 shows the drop in flowing rate of a discovery well directly after the time that two offsets were completed.

Increase in the permeability of limestone reservoirs by means of acid treatment benefits well-production rates.   The response varies in different districts, and the effect is generally to bring out the oil earlier and at a lower cost rather than to augment the total amount recovered. A greater total amount, of course, results when wells which have reached the economic limit as far as ordinary pumping is concerned are successfully acidized.   Figure 22 shows a Hunton lime well in Okfuskee County.   It was acidized early in 1938.   When examining properties of this type it is wise to study particularly the decline rate which followed the acid treatment, and to look for the possibility of earlier exhaustion.

Figure 23 shows the behavior of a Seminole well which responded only slightly to acid.   In November, 1930, it was brought in with an initial yield of 40,000 barrels per month; during 1932 it declined rapidly, was given a treatment of acid early in 1933 and a later retreatment in the same year.   In 1934 the oil yield declined to where some income from gas was the only means of continued operation until the end of 1936, when it was abandoned.

The production from a property which, after producing for several years from one sand, had its rate increased through the discovery and

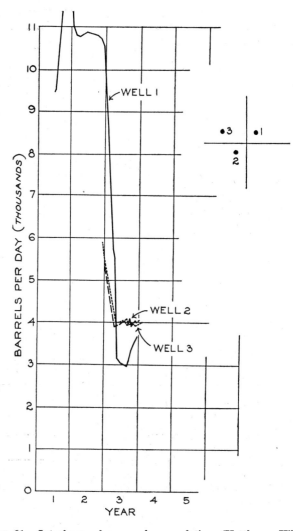

FIG. 21. Interference from nearby completions (Kettleman Hills).

development of a deeper sand is shown in Fig. 24. The form taken by this curve during the years 1932–33–34 is suggestive of properties which, after being only partially developed, are operated for some

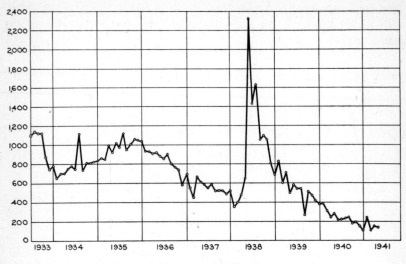

FIG. 22.   Acid treatment (Okfuskee County).

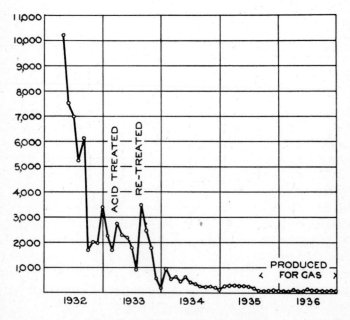

FIG. 23.   Acid treatment (Seminole).

time. Later, a resumption of drilling and an extension of the productive area improves the production, but it is rarely that the individual well yields approach the high points of well completions during the initial period.

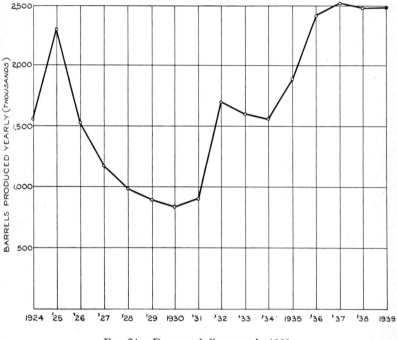

Fig. 24. Deep sand discovery in 1931.

The discovery of deeper sands often brings about new, high figures in production rates. This has happened at Salt Creek, Wyoming (Fig. 25), a field of many case history experiences, which include the progressive discoveries of deeper sands, a long flowing period, early introduction of gas recycling, and finally a unit project which blankets nearly the entire field.

The later life of a Santa Fe Springs well that was drilled during 1924 is shown in Fig. 26. This sort of record leaves the appraiser almost helpless when asked to judge its future. The well is reported to have been restricted late in 1932, so that the reduced production through 1934 was ascribed to curtailment. This may be true, but it is doubtful; and certainly, subsequent to the middle of 1935, it has been produced to capacity. During the early years the gravity of the oil sold improved about one degree, probably the result of improved dehydration treatment. The most important illustrative feature is the percentage of water contained in the total fluid that was raised in order to secure the oil.

The long-continued and uniform water percentages at 70 per cent during 1935–36, at 92 per cent in 1940, and then at 90 per cent during 1940–41 indicate only that for these periods the record is valueless

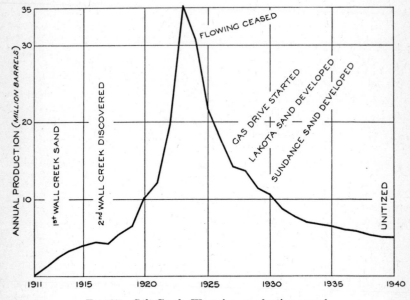

FIG. 25.   Salt Creek, Wyoming, production record.

except for showing that the well produced much water. Some irresponsible pumper or gauger simply reported the figures and they were not challenged. Oil wells do not behave that way. But the oil report must be substantially correct because it had to check with the pipe-line runs and the monthly inventories.

Attempting to guess how long this well will produce profitably, knowing that the controlling factor is the upswinging water curve, is a typical illustration of the problem with a great number of wells. When they produce fluid containing water ranging from 70 per cent to 95 per cent, they often hang on for a long period; then, when they do go out, they do so overnight. The time when the water will snuff them out is unpredictable. Therefore, a bank loan, secured by one-well production, is bad business and ill advised.

Additional Oil Recoveries. An important source of oil supply has become the winning of amounts beyond those obtained with the conventional methods. This is an impressive element when its potentialities for the future are considered, for currently nearly six hundred projects in thirteen states are now concerned with this type of opera-

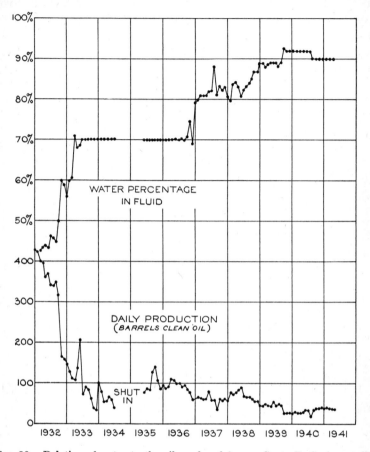

Fig. 26. Relation of water to the oil produced from a Santa Fe Springs well.

tion through water flood, gas recycling, repressuring, pressure maintenance, etc. A moderate estimate of their average effect is more than one million barrels per project.

Many occurrences of oil are known which cannot now be operated profitably, but which may become available through improved technique in production methods. Peckham records (in the Tenth Census of the United States) that in the early days of Oil Creek one operator had a conviction that to 10 feet in the sand was a sufficient depth to drill any well. The further recovery from these wells, which were

purchased from him after their short life of production from the top
10 feet of sand, proved a highly profitable undertaking.

The classical example of this type of operation has been the water
drive, or "flood," at Bradford, Pennsylvania. This has resulted in
very substantial additional quantities of oil. Water, injected into the
oil sands through a series of wells, scours the sand and carries the oil
to nearby withdrawal wells. The process has been improved in technique and applied in a number of districts, but not always with success,
because all oil fields are not alike.

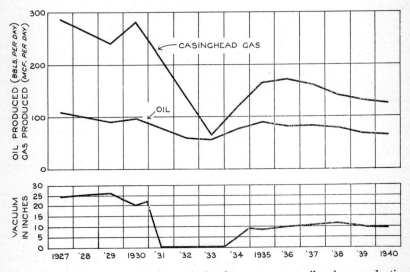

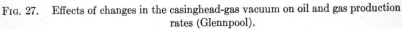

FIG. 27.   Effects of changes in the casinghead-gas vacuum on oil and gas production
rates (Glennpool).

Natural gasoline may be considered a byproduct, although it is an
oil. The additional income provided by it has lengthened the productive life of many wells. Application of vacuum to the casinghead gas
lines has expedited the recovery of gas in many fields, and, in areas
such as Glennpool where water drive is not an agency contributing to
the reservoir energy, it has probably increased the ultimate oil recovery. The effects of change in the degree of vacuum on wells in that
field is shown in Fig. 27. The contribution to earnings from this
source has a particular significance there in the light of the fact that
many properties produce more barrels of natural gasoline than barrels
of oil.

A reversal of vacuum application is the injection of gas or of air into
the sand for a purpose analogous to the water flood in scouring the

sand and sweeping the oil along. Air is not held in good repute; it corrodes the pipe, forms explosive mixtures, and seems to cause a certain drying up of the sand. Typical response to gas drive is shown in the record of a Tonkawa property (Fig. 28).

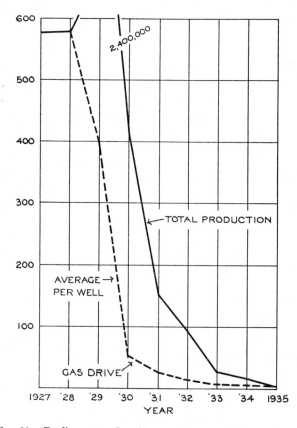

FIG. 28. Decline rate reduced by applying gas drive (Tonkawa).

Many other unique and clever devices and processes are applicable in production practice. They apply both to improved mechanical finishing of wells and accompanying lessening of costs and to increased recoveries. Their ultimate effect is more oil at less cost.

SALT DOMES

Probably the most uncertain and elusive of oil reserves encountered by the appraiser is the class associated with piercement-type salt domes. Dips are usually steep and the faulting extensive and highly irregular. The oil occurs in beds which have suffered great deformation; these beds encircle and dip away from the injected salt plug. The salt plug may be simple or irregular in outline; usually it is circular or oval in shape, occasionally extending on top as an overhang or in a mushroom position. The fields also lack uniformity in size; the cores of salt are as much as 1½ miles in diameter, and the area which has suffered distortion is as much as 4 miles. In most of these structures blank and unproductive sections occur in portions of the encircling band.

The very high yields provided by certain salt-dome flanks cannot well be accounted for by the thickness and areal extent of the known sands. A spacing which averages a well to 3 acres or less on a band 500 feet in width is often found to be highly profitable. But until several wells have been completed and have indicated a productivity behavior, the estimates of oil-reserves at a new field can afford little more than the form of an intelligent comparison with similar situations in the same region.

Occasionally cap-rock production is found to have accumulated in porous portions of limestone caps which surmount the salt, as at Spindletop, Texas, and at Leeville, Louisiana.

NATURAL GAS

The gases which constitute natural gas belong chiefly in the paraffin series. The chief constituent is methane. Impurities are nitrogen, carbon dioxide, helium, and hydrogen sulphide. The gas comes to the surface in two forms, which result from the two principal types of its occurrence underground.

1. Alone and unassociated with oil, in reservoirs which contain gas only. This is called dry gas or rock gas, and in some legal uses it is designated natural gas. The occurrences may be near oil fields or they may be remotely situated from any oil developments. The geographical situation of a gas supply has an important bearing on marketing and value. Oil has the advantage in that it can be moved from place to place with greater flexibility, can be stored, and adapted to changing demands.

2. With the oil produced from oil wells. This is called casinghead gas or wet gas. It is associated with the oil in the reservoir, either in solution in the oil or as free gas above the oil. When brought to the surface and separated from the oil, it is processed in a plant for the removal of the natural gasoline vapors and is then used for fuel and field operating purposes, or is sold, or is blown to the air.

In measurements the assumed absolute atmospheric pressure is 14.4

pounds. Sales are usually conducted at a ¼-pound base above, or 14.65 pounds absolute, and at 60° F temperature. Under many of the earlier contracts the gas is bought from the producer at a 2-pound base (16.4 pounds absolute) and sold at a ¼-pound base.

Dry-gas Reserves. Gas is more fluid than oil and its capacity for expansion expedites its recovery. A greater portion of the underground content is eventually recoverable.

The dry gas, produced from wells which yield gas only and no appreciable quantities of liquid, is the principal source of supply for the large marketing systems which collect and distribute over wide areas for both industrial and domestic consumption. Casinghead gas augments this supply and in California provides more than 90 per cent of all the gas distributed, the few dry-gas fields serving chiefly as a backlog with which to meet peak-load conditions.

Estimates of the available supplies of the recoverable dry gas in a field are made either by the saturation method, comparable to the volumetric method of estimating the oil content of a reservoir from the known data for area, pore space, etc.; or by the pressure-volume method, which is based on the observed drop in pressure that has occurred within the reservoir, owing to the withdrawal of a known volume of gas.

Saturation Method. This volumetric estimate is computed primarily from the areal extent of the reservoir, the porosity of the sand, and the pressure at which the gas is contained. The chief adjustments which will be considered are the connate water, the reservoir temperature, the compressibility factor as influenced by deviations from Boyle's Law, the residual pressure in the sand at the time of practical exhaustion, and the encroachment of edge water on the decline in reservoir pressure.

Connate water is variable, is as much as 40 per cent, and is difficult to measure with convincing accuracy. It is probably equivalent in most reservoirs to 10 per cent or 12 per cent of the interstitial space, and is often more than that.

Temperature correction is based on the fact that the volume of a gas varies directly with the absolute temperature. Most reservoir temperatures range from 110° F to 190° F, and often may be estimated from the known prevailing temperatures in nearby developed fields. The correction to bring the gas volume to the standard surface temperature of 60° F, which is the base used for measurements in the industry, for a subsurface temperature of 140° F, would be

$$\frac{460 + 60}{460 + 140} = \frac{520}{600} = 0.867$$

The effect of the reservoir pressure is expressed by Boyle's Law — the volume of a perfect gas varies inversely with the pressure. With an assumed atmospheric pressure of 14.4 pounds, the correction to bring the volume of the reservoir gas content at a pressure of 3,000 pounds down to atmospheric volume would be

$$\frac{3,000 + 14.4}{14.4} = 209.3$$

The *estimated gas content* of a reservoir is expressed

$$A \times P \times T \times R \times 43,560$$

where A = acre-feet of gas-containing sand

P = porosity expressed as a fraction of the sand volume

T = temperature correction to 60° F

R = pressure ratio expressed in atmospheres of 14.4 pounds

43,560 = cubic feet per acre-foot of volume.

Thus, if a gas reservoir has been ascertained to contain 60,000 acre-feet of sand volume having an average porosity of 20 per cent, a temperature of 170° F, and a rock or static pressure of 3,400 pounds, the equation for the gas content would be

$$60,000 \times 0.20 \times \frac{460 + 60}{460 + 170} \times \frac{3,400 + 14.4}{14.4} \times 43,560$$

$$= 102,204,828,000 \text{ cubic feet} \quad \text{or} \quad 102,204,828 \text{ mcf}$$

Boyle's Law does not hold strictly true, and the departures from it vary with gases that contain different percentages of constituents at different pressures. Except in situations where great precision is sought, this factor is negligible because it is clouded by other influences of greater moment, such as encroachment of water. The extent of encroachment of water is usually unmeasurable; and it is convenient to combine all the factors which are known to exist, but which are too intangible for definite expression, into one recovery factor, which in itself is entirely a matter of opinion. This composite recovery factor should not be assumed to be more than 60 per cent, even after the estimated residual pressure has been fixed.

The *estimated recoverable gas* is expressed

$$V \times C \times F$$

where V = reservoir gas volume, as derived above

C = pressure correction to the residual base

F = recovery factor

If in the foregoing illustration the residual pressure is assumed to be 200 pounds and the recovery factor 60 per cent, then the estimated recoverable gas is

$$102{,}204{,}828 \text{ mcf} \times \frac{(3{,}400 - 200) + 14.4}{3{,}400 + 14.4} \times 0.60 = 57{,}704{,}846 \text{ mcf}$$

Pressure-volume Method. During the period when gas is being produced from a reservoir, the expansion of the gas which remains is closely a function of the pressure, and the pressure drop reflects the volume of the gas that has been removed. The temperature of the gas in a reservoir remains practically unchanged during production.

The pressure-volume method is derived from this basis. It assumes roughly that, after a known quantity of gas has been removed and the wells have been shut in for a time sufficient to reveal the static pressure to which it has become adjusted, the computed amount of gas taken out thus far per pound of pressure decline indicates the remaining available quantity.

Assume that the closed-in pressure of a new field is initially 2,880 pounds. After a session of withdrawals the wells are shut in until they fail to build up any further material pressure increase, and they then show a pressure of 2,720 pounds. During the period the amount of gas taken out has been 400,000,000 cubic feet. Thus the withdrawal has been equivalent to 400 ÷ (2,880 − 2,720), or 2,500,000 cubic feet per pound of pressure drop. The indicated remaining volume of gas, then, is 2,500,000 feet times 2,720, or 6,800,000,000 feet. Assuming a residual pressure in the reservoir of 250 pounds, the recoverable gas is expressed

$$2{,}500{,}000 \times (2{,}700 - 250) = 6{,}175{,}000{,}000 \text{ cubic feet}$$

Estimates of this kind, made during the early life of a field, are little more than generalities, however, because they seem to lead to results substantially below the actual capacity of the gas reservoir.

Casinghead Gas. This is the gas produced with the oil from oil wells. In the reservoir it either is dissolved in the oil or is a surplus or free gas, dissociated from the oil and above it in the form of a gas cap. Estimates of casinghead gas are generally based on an assumption that the current gas-oil ratio will continue indefinitely. The ratio does vary to a considerable extent under different operating conditions and withdrawal rates, so that any estimate of this nature which relies on the relation of the gas volume to the content of recoverable oil may prove wide of the mark. When estimates based upon an assumption of a fixed gas-oil ratio are not confirmed by experience, it usually happens that the volumes of gas are greater than were anticipated.

Casinghead gas is processed for the removal of the vapors which make natural gasoline, at absorption plants where the gas is passed through oils that dissolve and retain the gasoline vapors. The gasoline is removed by distillation from the oil, which is returned in a continuous stream to the absorbing towers. The rates of recovery range from 0.5 gallon to 10 gallons per mcf; a yield of less than the former rate is seldom profitable if the gas requires compression. The richness generally increases as a field ages; and, although this increase is seldom sufficient to compensate for the decline in volume of gas production, it does take up much of the slack, and often it does so completely. The common experience, early in the natural gasoline industry of over-estimates of future gasoline outputs, was caused chiefly by the failure in new projects at flush fields to allow sufficiently for rapid declines in production rates from the oil wells of both the oil and the accompanying gas.

In valuation practice it is common to ascertain the amounts of gasoline and of gas obtained per barrel of oil produced, together with the revenue provided by them, and to combine the two income sources with the price of the oil into one unit amount of income per barrel for oil, gas, and gasoline.

Some of the unstable oils in natural gasoline which are lighter than pentane evaporate and weather off. They are collected and are readily liquefied and held in liquid form in low-pressure containers. This product is the butane of commerce.

CONDENSATE

Occurrences of gas which have greatly increased in importance during recent years are the condensate fields, known more commonly among oil operators as " gas-distillate " fields. The latter term is misleading since the product is a condensate and not a distillate.

Pressure and temperature conditions in these fields cause the fluids in the reservoir to be in a gaseous state, or vapor phase. As distinguished from the usual forms of oil-field occurrences where the gas is in solution in the oil, here the oil is in solution in the gas. The usual dry-gas fields supply gas which contains from 0.1 to 0.5 gallon per mcf. These deep condensate fields carry $\frac{1}{2}$ gallon to 4 or more gallons. The fact that their content is in vapor phase makes them readily recoverable by reason of their high fluidity.

High pressures prevail in the reservoirs. When gas is withdrawn and is reduced in pressure or when the pressure in the reservoirs is lowered by the removal of a portion of their content, the stability of the gaseous form ceases and a condensation takes place. This is " retrograde condensation," an expression that is used rather loosely. It is only with great difficulty that those who have grown up in the tradition that liquefaction of gases and vapors is accomplished by an increase of pressure are able to adjust themselves to this conception that a gas will condense to liquid form under the influence of a drop in pressure.

The product from these condensate wells is an oil rather than a gasoline or a distillate. It contains gasoline, kerosene distillate, and a considerable percentage of heavier fractions, and is distinguishably different in content and behavior from the natural gasoline derived from casinghead gas.

When the drop in pressure takes place within the underground reservoir, owing to large gas withdrawals, and this drop is sufficient in extent to cause condensation of liquids, these liquid portions become dissipated. Once spread out and attached to the grain particles in the sand, they are no longer recoverable. For this reason, a continued pressure maintenance inside a high pressure reservoir is essential in the effective removal of the oil and gasoline dissolved in a gas body. This rule holds whether the entire content is in gaseous phase or whether it exists as a gas cap above a body of gas-saturated liquid oil.

Pressure maintenance is accomplished by a cycle of operations which comprise (1) withdrawal of gas from the reservoir through wells situated at selected spots; (2) removal from the gas of its oil content; (3) compression and return of the dry gas to the reservoir through injection wells. The injection wells are placed so as to cause the returned gas to drive untreated gas ahead of it toward the withdrawal wells. The result, at least the objective, is maintenance of a suitable pressure within the reservoir to the end that condensation of oil within it is held at a minimum.

It is evident that such occurrences lend themselves to unitization and, in fact, are seldom commercially feasible except under a community effort and arrangement. The underground gas in its original state is the last word in fluidity. Failure to return dry gas and thereby to hold the reservoir pressure at a proper level can prevent the recovery of large volumes of oil. Under independent and individual operation of properties a single important producer who withdraws gas and fails to replace it can render a project unworkable. Cooperative treatment is essential.

Estimates of the volumes of gas contained in distillate fields follow the pattern of the volumetric determination in dry-gas fields, based on area and thickness of the formation, porosity, reservoir pressure, and temperature. The pressure-decline method is applicable to partly depleted fields, but dearth of full information often vitiates the estimates. Refinements of measurements or fine-haired corrections are seldom worth introducing into a computation because the elements of the deviation from Boyle's Law, the saturation factor, drainage efficiency, and recovery factor are only estimated within a fairly wide range.

A fresh-water condensate is produced along with the gas from distillate wells; it is present in vapor phase in the reservoir, usually in a proportion of 15 to 60 gallons per million cubic feet of gas. Connate salt water is present in small measure, but this is probably in liquid form. Saturation factors from 50 per cent to 70 per cent are used, and recoveries in about the same proportion. Tests conducted with gas under field operating conditions provide estimates of the recovery of oil and this unit, applied to the estimates of obtainable gas, supplies an estimate of the recoverable oil, expressed usually in terms of a stabilized butane-free oil.

WELL SPACING

Those factors to be weighed when the effect on the value of a property of the spacing of wells is considered are

Costs of wells, against the profit they will supply

Recoverable production per acre

Thickness and nature of the sand or lime

The radius of drainage, as suggested by the elements of oil viscosity, sand permeability, gas-cap features, gas in solution, probable gas-oil ratios

The spacing of wells in any pattern of development affects not only the costs but also the oil recoveries. In many types of reservoirs the number of necessary wells can be reduced greatly and the amount of oil ultimately gained can be increased under a program of relatively slow, orderly, and controlled oil withdrawals. The only important sacrifice would be the accelerated income from early flush-production rates.

But the valuation engineer encounters the problem of well spacing as something which he must accept as he finds it, both in his consideration of the amounts of oil to be obtained from the proved undeveloped properties and the costs which they will entail. A close spacing of wells results in high extraction from the property; wide spacing results in high recoveries per well but a decreased property total. Production efficiencies and deep drilling are leading away from close spacing.

If a 10-acre pattern is the rule in a field, the conclusions must follow an assumption that both this field custom and the insistence of the landowner will require a similar well density, notwithstanding that one well to 20 acres may be clearly shown to be a better economic practice for the working interest. If no spacing rule has become established in the area, then an assumed spacing and estimate of recoveries and costs is based on a mixture of well-conducted operations and expediency as the appraiser judges that they will emerge from the conflict between the offset competitive acreage developments, the inflexible lease conditions, the complacency of the landowner, and such regulations as the administrative agencies may enforce.

It may prove appropriate to take into account an additional 5-spot location when one is believed to be economically profitable, especially in the examination of a property for the type of buyer that drills them.

REFERENCES

RALPH ARNOLD, "Petroleum Resources of the United States," *Economic Geology*, 1915.

RALPH ARNOLD and others, *Manual for the Oil and Gas Industry*, 1919.

C. H. BEAL, *The Decline and Ultimate Production of Oil Wells*, U. S. Bureau of Mines, Bull. 177, 1919.

O. L. BRACE, *Factors Governing Estimation of Recoverable Oil in Sand Fields*, Vol. H, American Association of Petroleum Geologists, 1934.

JOHN F. CARRL, *Geology of the Oil Regions*, Second Geological Survey of Pennsylvania, 1880.

W. W. CUTLER, JR., *Estimation of Underground Oil Reserves*, U. S. Bureau of Mines, Bull. 228, 1924.

DODGE, PYLE, and TROSTEL, *The Estimation by Volumetric Methods of Recoverable Oil and Gas from Sands*, American Association of Petroleum Geologists, 1941.

Geology of Salt Dome Oil Fields, American Association of Petroleum Geologists, 1926.

EMBY KAYE, "Some Factors in the Economics of Recycling," *Petroleum Technology*, March, 1941.

L. C. LICHTY, *Measurement, Compression and Transportation of Natural Gas*, 1924.

PACIFIC COAST STUDY GROUP, Bibliography and Abstract of Papers on *Reservoir Conditions and Mechanics*, American Association of Petroleum Geologists, 1940.

PATTEN and IVEY, "Phase Equilibria in High-condensate Wells," *Oil Weekly*, Dec. 12, 1928.

PYLE and SHERBORNE, "Core Analysis," *Transactions of the American Institute of Mining and Metallurgical Engineers*, 1939.

R. J. SCHILTHUIS, "Connate Water in Oil and Gas Sands," *Transactions of the American Institute of Mining and Metallurgical Engineers*, 1938.

R. J. SCHILTHUIS, "Reservoir Energy and Oil Production," *Oil and Gas Journal*, Oct. 17, 1935.

J. S. SWEARINGEN, "Predicting Wet Gas Recovery," *Oil Weekly*, Dec. 25, 1939.

J. P. UMPLEBY, "Increasing the Extraction of Oil by Water-flooding," *Petroleum Development and Technology*, 1925.

CHAPTER V
ELEMENTS IN A VALUATION

Oil-field conditions vary so widely from one area to another, and even in the same field they change so importantly with the passage of time, that no single fixed valuation procedure can be applied to all the different situations. It is more orderly to examine the various factors which react on values, and then to review the methods of their application and suitability to the different circumstances which occasion a valuation.

The most important single factor is the one described in Chapter IV — the estimated recoverable oil. As to properties which are fairly developed and the facts known, engineers' estimates of the recoverable oil will not differ greatly. Opinions do differ concerning how much reliance should be placed on these estimates. Some engineers feel comfortably secure that they are within 5 or 10 per cent of the correct answer. Others consider that, even with a full background of facts and with a freedom from those uncertainties inherent in this kind of an undertaking, the best that should be expected from a carefully prepared estimate of oil reserves is that it prove to be within plus or minus 25 per cent of the correct figure which only time will disclose.

The latter view appears to be the sound one; but, whichever may be more nearly correct, it is true that the valuation of oil wells remains an uncertain and difficult undertaking if for no other reason than the indefinite nature of these oil reserves. The uncertainties increase with the introduction of factors which relate to the worth of the oil. Such are the rates of oil withdrawals, the prices of oil and gas, the costs, each of which causes the values of the oil reserves and of the producing properties to fall within a much wider range. Some of these factors, such as prices and costs, enter either directly or indirectly into every valuation. Others are encountered only occasionally, but when they are found to exist they may prove to be of the first importance. An absence of a market for the oil, or the presence of a lessor whose exacting control of developments and operations renders the recovery of the oil unduly expensive, is thus classified. When the appraiser examines a situation, a long line of such factors pass mentally before him and he selects those which are material to the current job. The omission or the failure to discern some significant element in a valuation can have serious effects. It does happen, and the appraiser always fears that it may happen to him.

THE OIL

Petroleum has been defined in several ways; the word is generally used to describe mineral liquid oil. As found in nature, mineral liquid oil has a great variation of physical and chemical characteristics. In addition to the many kinds of hydrocarbons, impurities occur in the form of compounds of oxygen, sulphur, and nitrogen, all of which, except certain sulphur compounds, are not oily. Field production operations give little attention to the chemical analysis of oil; the chief interest is in the physical property of weight, or gravity. For a long time gravity was widely accepted as indicating with sufficient closeness the gasoline content of the oil, and hence its relative value for the manufacture of products. Along with improved refinery technique this index has come to have less and less significance as a measure of its utility, but it is doubtful that it will ever be supplanted in the producing fields as a means of identification.

Originally the price of crude oil did not depend on the gravity, except to the extent that in a general way the gravity and the quality of the oil in a district influenced the price offered for it. It was not until January, 1923 that a differential was set up in the Mid-Continent area with a sliding price schedule governed by gravity. A flat price continues to be paid in a number of areas, but in the districts of large production the higher gravity crudes bring the higher prices.

Crude oil is measured in barrels of 42 United States gallons, as of 60° F temperature, equal approximately to 35 British imperial gallons. Minor quantities are moved by tank car, steamer, barge, truck, etc., but the great bulk is transported to refineries through pipe lines. Delivery is made from the seller's tanks into the buyer's pipe line, the tanks having been strapped (measured) by the pipe-line company and a tank table prepared for showing its capacity at each unit of height. The gauger, representing the buyer, measures the height of oil (the high gauge), reads the temperature from a thermometer suspended in the oil, opens a valve, and allows the oil to be pumped into the buyer's pipe line. When the tank is nearly empty the gauger returns, locks the valve on the discharge line, and delivers a run ticket to the producer. On this run ticket have been recorded the tests of the sample for gravity and percentage of impurities.

The disposition of the oil thereafter receives little consideration from the producer, who regards refiners and marketers only as rather necessary evils. His has been the glory of the chase; once the capture is made and he has received a check for the oil his interest ceases. Settlement is made on the basis of a division order, a document signed by all those who have an interest in the oil, and it is used by the purchasing company as an authorization in the allocation of the oil payments.

Marketing. The sale of crude oil is generally rather simple, and the rank and file of producers may seem to have little opportunity for the exercise of merchandising talents. The pipe lines of the large purchasing companies weave through the oil fields, and these companies post buying prices for the crude. The schedules are usually identical for identical oils. It may be that producers at times have failed to receive equitable prices for their oil; but there is much for which they should be grateful in generally having had buyers ready to take their oil and to pay for it promptly, without tribute to brokers or middlemen. Without this widespread response of buyers able to meet situations in a big way, the little producer would have had a genuine marketing and distributing problem on his hands.

Well-managed pipe-line companies rate their " connections " (independent producers whose oil they buy) as a valuable asset; give them advice and old maps, lend them money, and in other ways seek a cordial relationship. The smaller buyers often pay premiums above the posted market prices in order to prevail on the producer for his oil. At other times hot crude, produced in excess of recognized allotments, may be sold at substantial discounts to the less exacting buyers.

Price. Market demand for oil establishes the intensity of production operations and the search for new sources of supply and, in theory at least, it determines the price. But the outcome of exploration cannot be forecast, the extent of the discoveries ahead is entirely unpredictable, and the consequent erratic results have been reflected in alternating periods of a dearth of supply and of excessive over-production. Growth of the industry has broadened the uses and the extent of demand, so that a single important discovery now lacks the market-breaking tendency of former days. Added to this is the control, exercised through proration and curtailment, that effects the present-day more orderly withdrawal of oil. Disturbances like those that followed the discovery and development of Cushing and Cleveland, Midway-Sunset, Signal Hill, and East Texas have come to have less striking effects on price structures.

It has been a characteristic of the successful oil operators to have a nice sense of the value of their crude oil and of the price trend and to have a flair for the difficult operation of selling it to advantage. The choice of crude and its purchase is a primary requisite in a successful refinery operation. Unwise commitments to purchase crude over a long period at a fixed price have occasioned severe punishment to refining companies.

The influence of the crude price extends in many directions and to all phases of the business. It affects income, the economic limit of a stripper well, the availability of oil reserves awaiting secondary recovery. It has always been the most important known factor in regulating the volume of drilling activity. A characteristic upturn in production follows the announcement of a crude-price increase; a comparable sag follows a reduction in price. A reason that the majority of the valuations which are in common circulation appear to be on the high side is that these valuations are usually prepared for the obvious purpose of selling a property or a security, and such activities are usually conducted during the cycles of high crude prices with their accompanying better-than-average earnings.

The wide swings in the average price received for crude oil during the period since 1876, in the United States and in California, are shown in Fig. 29. The post World War 1 inflation of 1920 is especially apparent in contrast with the nose dives taken by prices during 1921 and 1922.

The current crude prices are found in the trade journals and are shown as the amounts paid by buying companies for the oil they do purchase, and these prices represent the " posted market price " as nearly as does anything that is available to the appraiser. Buyers no longer engage to take all the oil that is offered to them. Formerly they posted at a designated spot in their office a schedule of prices, which usually followed the lead of some one company in each district or region. Great mental effort has been put into the attempt to compose a legally attack-proof definition of posted price, worded so that it does not name the Standard Oil Company. This continues to be a favorite intellectual exercise for attorneys.

An estimate of price variations paid for oils of the same gravity but in different areas is supplied in the following table.

July, 1941, Crude-oil Prices

Gravity	Kansas Oklahoma	North Louisiana	West Texas	Gulf Coast	Salt Creek Wyoming	California	Turner Valley
22°	$0.81–$0.89	$0.94	$0.76	$1.12	$0.96	$0.83–$1.02	
32°	1.09	1.14	0.96	1.32	1.04	1.07– 1.29	$1.08

It is not to be inferred that oils of similar gravities have identical

qualities or values.   The contrary is true, and for that reason buyers
have become increasingly selective in their choice of crudes.   The
small independent refineries are especially able to offer premiums for
oils of particular desirability

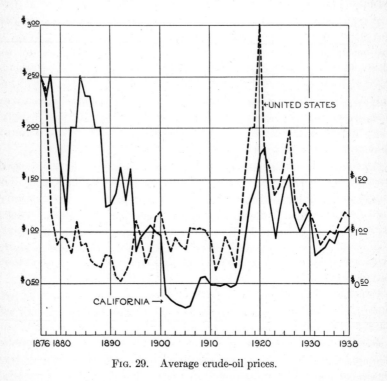

FIG. 29.   Average crude-oil prices.

Frequently the engineer finds himself asked to forecast the price of
crude oil, a requirement which places a great strain on his imagination
if he happens to be a realist and disclaims having the Old Testament
gift of prophecy.   In general, it is unwise to forecast.   The price of
crude results from the relation of supply to demand and, notwithstanding that proration and curtailment are productive of conservation and
a reduction of waste, it is true that their inception has been in the
efforts to fit supply to demand, with at least a tiny hope in the background that either sustained or improved prices would result.

Many interesting efforts have been made to forecast crude prices,
and to derive formulas for this purpose, in the interest of introducing
and supporting them in a valuation.   The fact remains that these
occasions arise when crude is in demand, when the discoveries of new
sources are not keeping up with the amounts withdrawn and an antici-

pated shortage of crude is receiving attention. Considerations of conservation and of posterity then become the watchwords, and a resulting departure from a straight-line estimate of future crude prices invariably takes the form of an ascending curve. One has yet to see an estimate of future prices with a downward trend.

A committee of engineers, appointed in 1920 to study and to forecast the price of crude oil in California, concluded that the appraisers, in estimating the prices of oil for the period following 1924, should use an average annual increase of 17 per cent for fuel oil until it should have reached the price of $2.00 per barrel; and that thereafter the annual increase should be continued but in diminishing percentages; that the ultimate peak for crude oil should be $4.00 per barrel. Actually, 20 years thereafter, fuel oil was $0.70 per barrel, and ample splendid refining crude was available at $1.10.

An alternative course of some merit is that of invoking the average past price of crude over a stated period — of 3 years or 5 years. The object is to remove the effect of a local, and presumably temporary, high or low price which may be in effect at a specific time during a period that contains a number of minor changes. Again, it is observable that this course has generally been introduced at a time when the price was low, as compared with the average of prices over the stated period.

Generally it is preferable to avoid introducing into the primary portion of a valuation any projected variable price of crude oil as a basis for the determination of property value. It is not necessary to do so; a definitive estimate of value that is predicated upon a single conception of price is the direct and simple course. The account can then be accompanied with supplemental showings as to the probable effects on earnings and on values of plus-or-minus crude-price deviations from the original. Use of the current price has a high degree of objectivity; and certainly until beset by a period of years of continued crude shortages and of failure of exploration and of lack of discoveries of new sources to keep up with the withdrawals, it is unwarranted to assume any price changes other than the minor ups and downs which have marked the past 15-year period.

Once the price basis is fixed, the next move of the appraiser is to learn the gravity of the oil in question. One average gravity and its price may be sufficiently accurate, but in practice the gravity is often found to swing from time to time within two or three degrees, and it is preferable to bring the figure within closer limits. The needed information is supplied in the sales and shipment records.

The original memoranda are the run tickets received from the purchaser. They show the gravity of the oil contained in every tank delivery. Unless an original record is required, the entries from these documents are assembled more handily in the seller's pipe-line ledger record of oil sales. The buyer's monthly statements of oil purchased show the quantities of oil taken in each gravity class and the amounts due, and from the totals in the statements the average return per barrel is readily derived. This figure is the most satisfactory composite index for use in a valuation. Care should be taken to insure that the monthly average return figure is not distorted by reason of price changes during the month.

The monthly statements of buyers show not only the record tank runs but also the disposition of the entire amount to the various owners, in line with the allocation contained in the division order. These statements serve examiners as a quick check on ownerships and titles since the important buying companies are fairly assured as to the titles of oil for which they are paying.

A change in the price of crude during the latter period of an appraisal is a confusing affair and causes much recalculation. The influence on the valuations of acreage and unproved lands is less than on the oil reserves and the developed oil properties. The effect of an upward price change is to improve not only the outlook for profits, which become increased in greater proportion than the ratio of the crude-price increase, but also the estimated barrels of reserves by extending the estimated productive life of the wells to a new and further deferred economic limit point.

The Gas

Natural gas is the perfect fuel; it is unfortunate that it is not more widely available. It is odorless, clean, nonpoisonous, easily and efficiently applied to use. Being a mixture of several gases whose qualities differ, it varies in physical characteristics and heating values. The chief nonburning constituents are nitrogen and carbon dioxide; they occur irregularly and usually in small proportion. The inflammable ingredients are the hydrocarbons; the chief member is methane, which has a heating value of 1,008 Btu per cubic foot.

Unlike oil, it cannot be readily stored in large volume, and it has no posted price. Distribution and the retail price are subject to the control of state public utility regulatory bodies; generally the sale from producers to marketers is an individual matter arranged between them. Gas companies are adroit and resourceful bargainers. Sometimes they offer an established price for all the gas purchased in a locality; more often it will be found that prices in the same locality differ materially, even though the gas is under similar conditions of volume, pressure, and rates of delivery.

The price is influenced both by the supply and by the costs of competitive sources of power and fuel such as coal, fuel oil, and electricity. Price clauses in sales contract are often tied to the competitive fuels, so as to move up and down with them, sometimes with and sometimes without a ceiling. In general the price received by the producer ranges from 2 cents to 10 cents per mcf, with higher rates up to 60 cents where conditions are unusual. The several factors which influence this aside from competitive conditions are the market outlets, the delivery pressure, and the load conditions. Heating value of the gas is of less importance.

Gas which is remotely situated from industrial centers and areas of domestic use has little value, unless the industries are moved to it, as has happened with brickyards, glass plants, and carbon black factories. A cool, wet region which is free from abrupt and extreme temperature changes is ideal for domestic loads. Industrial loads which come on irregularly are less desirable. Gas which is to be delivered at a continuous and relatively uniform rate of flow commands lower prices than those quantities required only occasionally for meeting peak loads. Interruptible load gas, usually sold in competition with fuel oil or coal, brings a lower price because its service is the first to be discontinued at times of shortage in supply.

Most gas pipe lines operate at initial pressures of about 400 pounds per square inch. Gas supplied at lower pressures may entail an expense for compression, generally ranging from 1 cent to $2\frac{1}{2}$ cents per thousand cubic feet. In one form of agreement, the producer delivers a stated quantity of gas regularly, and stands prepared to supply some much larger quantities during periods of peak loads. This arrangement is logical and is often necessary, but in those fields where the permeability of the reservoir sands is low or uncertain it may require the producer to drill more wells than would be needed except for this ready-to-serve feature.

The high fluidity of gas increases its response to capture through any well that is drilled into a reservoir, and especially into those reservoirs of high sand porosity and permeability. Careful attention to this feature is required in an appraisal. Gas reserves may be of great extent and yet may be so situated that their sales are small as compared with those from some neighboring small property whose operators have shown greater ability in selling the gas from their wells. Here the differentiation is especially marked between an estimate of the underground mineral, which lies beneath a given surface area, and the value of that mineral to the owner of the land, in the light of the sales situation and the effect on operating conditions of the law of capture.

Oil producers who sell substantial quantities of casinghead gas, obtained as a byproduct from the oil-production operations, find that the greatest demand for gas comes during the cold season, at just the time when their oil production is least desired. The oil property which has been encumbered by an agreement to supply during this peak period a quantity of gas which it can obtain only together with increased oil withdrawals is liable to excessive oil accumulations, or driven to producing from those wells where the gas-oil ratios are high.

Uses and markets for those gases which are not inflammable are limited. Those gases that are high in nitrogen are often characterized by a helium content, but this product has only one customer and does not pay off well. Carbon dioxide wells have engaged considerable attention as a source of gas from which to make Dry Ice, but thus far the industry has not attained any significant size. The costs and economics of ice manufacture and distribution are such that, in order to compete with water ice, the gas supply must be available at so low a price that the development of a sufficient supply to warrant the erection of a manufacturing plant is a doubtful venture. Carbon dioxide wells are not uncommon. Discovery of a new field usually goes through the cycle of the discovery excitement, the added interest when it is learned that the gas is inert and does not burn, the promotion of a local company to utilize this natural resource for the manufacture of Dry Ice, and then the lesson that the raw material is a relatively unimportant item in the commercial feasibility of the project.

Casinghead Gas and Natural Gasoline

Gas is not only compressible but is also soluble in oil. When gas is released from the underground reservoir and brought to the surface, the oil volume is reduced and the gas expands. In the reservoir the oil may be heavily saturated with gas, or it may contain relatively little gas. The former condition is accompanied by high formation pressures.

When the oil in the reservoir is completely saturated with gas and is surmounted by a gas cap, then high gas-oil ratios prevail. The ratio generally reduces with time, but this does not always happen. Removal of oil and gas from the reservoir and reduction of the formation pressure releases solution gas from the oil and tends to cause a gas cap to form where one did not exist previously.

Casinghead gas is the name commercially applied to the gas which occurs with the oil from oil wells. It contains vapors of those gases which, when condensed, comprise the fractions of natural gasoline. Two courses are followed for handling and treating the gas for gasoline recovery; a plant may be built, provided the extent of the property warrants, or the gas may be disposed to the operators of some nearby plant.

The modern absorption plant costs from $15,000 to $30,000 per million cubic feet of gas handled daily, the difference depending chiefly on the richness of the gas, the extent of the gathering lines, and the compression equipment required. For many years the operating pressures in absorption plants were held at pressures below 30 pounds on account of certain patent restrictions. This limitation has expired, and the operating pressures now conform to convenience and efficiency, to the 400-pound limit carried by the lines of the major purchasing and transportation companies. The costs for compression made necessary for the purpose of disposing of the gas, rather than for its treatment for gasoline recovery, are properly a sales and delivery cost and not a charge against gasoline expense.

Operating costs are as high as 5 cents per gallon of natural gasoline recovered. A high-pressure system where the gas requires no compression and is treated in large volumes may incur costs of less than 1 cent. A plant of middle size, operating on 5 to 20 million feet per day of gas, which yields 1 gallon per thousand cubic feet, will have costs of 2 to 3 cents per gallon (including allowances for depreciation), with another cent required if compression of the gas is necessary. Gases of greater richness reduce the costs somewhat. Increased costs result from more widespread gathering lines, a thinner yield, unbalanced and irregular supplies of gas, and from over-built plants. Almost invariably the output of casinghead gas increases in richness with a decrease in pressure and in volume of oil produced.

Inclusion of the revenue from gas and gasoline in the course of appraising an oil-producing property is usually carried out best by assuming an income or return from the oil in the amount per net barrel that these sources contribute. An individual plant of substantial size calls for a separate examination and appraisal, of which a study of the extent and estimated continuity of production and richness of the gas is an important part. The records of past gas-oil ratios and bottom-hole pressures and of the behavior of the gas cap indicate what to expect in the future.

But in the smaller and more local situations it is usually sufficient to ascertain the revenues derived from sales of gas and gasoline, expressed in terms of cents per barrel of oil produced, and to add them to the price of crude oil. This amount will fluctuate from a fraction of a cent per barrel, to 4 and 5 cents (common rates), or to as high as 50 cents or even more in those situations where gas-oil ratios and gas sales are high. The condition is then more nearly comparable to gas-cap or to gas-distillate withdrawals than to the usual occurrence of dissolved gas.

Some consideration and allowance are to be made where the records disclose that the gas sales are seasonal and that wells with high gas-oil ratios are being drawn on more freely during the winter when the gas supply is to be augmented. It may well be found that an early income from gas sales is being achieved at a sacrifice in the ultimate oil recovery.

Butane and *propane* are other commercial products obtained at natural gasoline plants, although propane is more often turned out at refineries. These are gases at normal temperatures and pressures. They weather off the surface of natural gasoline and are liquefied by compression and held as a liquid under low pressure. In liquid form at the plant they sell for $2\frac{1}{2}$ to 3 cents per gallon for lot deliveries.

GAS DISTILLATE

This important source of oil and gasoline, where these products occur in vapor phase only in a reservoir which either is only gaseous or is a gas cap of considerable size overlying a body of liquid oil, has become well recognized as requiring some forms of pressure-maintenance operations which can be conducted efficiently only as a unit for the entire reservoir. The liquid product (condensate or distillate) results from a condensation brought about by a reduction in the pressure, the action usually designated as retrograde condensation, although the term lacks fixed definition.

Plants for the recovery of the liquid from the gas either are the oil-absorption type or are designed and built for regenerative gas cooling. Each type of plant costs about $12,000 per million cubic feet of daily capacity. In addition, wells must be drilled for the withdrawal of the gas and for its subsequent injection and return to the gas sand. In a new project the well costs take up the greater portion of the investment expense.

Operating costs, aside from depreciation and taxes, are about $5.00 per million cubic feet of gas handled, with variations either way for size and adaptability and efficiency of the plant, pressures attained, character of the gas, and the product obtained. Depreciation of investment varies with the reserves and with the time factor within which the plant cost is to be amortized. On a 10-year life it is about $1,200 per year per million cubic feet of daily capacity, or about $3.35 per million cubic feet of gas handled. Account must also be made for amortization of well costs, leasehold depletion, and the royalties. In some areas the landowners have been prevailed on to accept a royalty rate of one-half the rate effective as to crude-oil production; but no standard procedure in this regard has become established, and the half royalty rate has been more generally invoked where the profit margins are narrow and a pressure maintenance project is initiated only after a field has become partly depleted.

The present worth of either gas-cap gas or of the dry gas which will remain in a gas-distillate reservoir after the recycling period, each of which represents a type of production that is to be obtained and sold at some distant date, is usually a secondary and uncertain item in a valuation.

Costs

Costs have changed since the days in May, 1859, when Drake with his family arrived at Titusville, Pennsylvania, for the purpose of exploiting the oil springs on Oil Creek. At the American Hotel he, his wife, their two children, and a horse boarded for $6.50 per week. The scope for play in an expense account was limited.

The price of a product is in itself of no great consequence unless considered by the standard of both its costs and its relation to the prices of other products. The cost of a barrel of oil has received much study by many agencies and without too much definition of what is contemplated when the term is used, so that the results diverge widely in points of view and the published conclusions. In the mind of one narrator it means the entire scope of activities of a producing concern, including the exploration for properties, their acquisition, the rental payments, the drilling and pumping, insurance, supervision, and taxes of all kinds. In other accounts many of these items have been omitted without a clear indication of the eliminations.

Accountants hold widely different views regarding their practices and their place in the scheme of things. The method of handling a cost record can control the outcome to an entirely misleading extent. Much can be said in favor of a uniform system of accounting for the producing oil companies whose records are disclosed to the investing public by reason of their securities' being listed on exchanges. As it is now, no fixed meaning or limitation in scope is recognized for many of the expressions contained in the profit-and-loss statements of different companies.

Probably the average cost to the oil operator of finding, acquiring, and producing a barrel of Mid-Continent crude oil is about $1.25. In California the rate is somewhat less, and that is also probably true of the Gulf Coast and western Texas regions. The major subdivisions which combine to reach these units may be grouped under five headings — acquisition, development, production operations, taxes, and administration. The last two items are frequently contained in the one class designated " overhead."

Acquisition. It comprises exploration and discovery, geology, scouting, purchase of lands, leases and proved properties, drilling dry holes, and contributions toward dry-hole completions.

Of all the elements which contribute to the cost of bringing a barrel of oil to the surface, the item of acquisition is the one which has the greatest variation and influences most effectively the success or failure of an oil company. Oil reserves are obtained either through exploration and discovery or through purchase from the successful finder. Some concerns are less successful at exploration, and in their purchases of properties from others they establish standards of prices and of values.

The landowner, of course, takes no share in the exploration risks and expenditures. These costs are assumed by the lessee, and either they may be slight or they may run into very large figures. In a typical and average successful company, whose operations are sufficiently extensive and widespread to supply the benefits of diversification, the average cost through discovery effort is about 35 or 40 cents per barrel. The actual total economic cost is manifestly greater because this unit must carry the load of all the scattered losses incurred by amateurs in their haphazard exploration, and their average record of discovery is markedly less successful.

The cost of finding and buying lessee oil of good quality in the ground which has been discovered by another person is greater than 40 cents. Company records in this field of inquiry are difficult to analyze even when the basic information is made available. Generally such data are carefully guarded; but it is interesting to observe, aside from theories and the complexities of modern accounting which obscure simple conclusions, the extent to which some of the very successful companies owe their growth chiefly to the ability of one or more geologists who have a genuine flair for finding oil and are abetted in their work by a well-directed land department. Other companies have achieved their position, on the other hand, because of an uncanny capacity to measure the meaning and significance of a new oil-field discovery and because they have the nerve and willingness to support their judgement with their money.

Oil in the ground which is proved up but not drilled up is, therefore, a unit of commerce. As such, it engages the attention of the appraiser and is found to sell for as much as 50 cents or more per barrel, depending on quality, crude prices, costs, and other factors. Almost any crude for which there is a market and which can be profitably obtained is fairly worth 10 cents per barrel in the ground.

Development. The costs of development include the drilling and completion of wells and such improvements as roads, buildings, pipe lines, tanks, natural-gasoline plants, and power installations. The costs here as elsewhere vary considerably and are changing constantly, owing both to fundamental economic conditions beyond the control of the operator and to improvements in technical methods of drilling and production. Any account of costs which goes into great detail would soon be out-of-date and misleading; for this reason the aim here will be to indicate instead the approximate ranges within which costs fall during the course of the usual oil-field developments.

The drilling and completion of wells constitute the chief item of expense for development. Shallow wells which are drilled with a portable outfit may cost as little as $1,000; in the hilly districts of Kentucky it may require a greater outlay to move the drilling rig to the well location than the cost of the well itself. Costs on the high side, apart from the exceptional experiences with mishaps and long fishing jobs, are more than $200,000 for the 14,000-foot exploration wells at isolated points. The initial exploratory well costs more than the wells which come later, and the continued development of a field brings lowered costs with improved methods and increased competition among contractors.

Slim-hole drilling is an innovation which has brought about some marked cost reductions, chiefly through pipe economies. As its name implies, it includes holes of small diameter. Upper water is cemented off through perforations in the finishing string, thus permitting the use of a relatively shallow string of conductor pipe and of only one long string. An 8,000- to 9,000-foot well, drilled in this way, with $8\frac{5}{8}$-inch casing at 900 feet, can be completed with $4\frac{1}{2}$-inch casing inside it to the bottom of the hole or to a point above the sand.

Tangible costs of wells are those costs which represent the physical property, such as derrick, pipe, and other equipment; they are capitalized and retired through annual charges to depreciation. The *intangible costs* are the labor, fuel, power, freight and hauling, water, repairs, and the other items which provide no salvage return after the completion of the well or which have no physical identity. This class of costs may either be capitalized and retired through annual charges or else written off as an expense item in the income account during the year in which incurred. Generally the former course is followed. The intangible costs make up 60 to 70 per cent of the entire well cost; the percentage is greater with the shallow wells, the deep slim holes, and the other wells where the casing pattern requires less pipe than usual.

The costs of the completed wells shown in the table below are suggestive of the general range. The individual depths and costs differ somewhat; and in any specific situation, especially if it is of a controversial nature, detailed and definite data should be obtained, usually from supply houses and contractors. Wells completed in the same field but in different properties and under different managements will vary somewhat; the differences will be found to narrow down when carried out under contract.

WELL COSTS

	Field	Depth Range (Feet)	Cost Range (Dollars)
Kansas — Oklahoma	Creek County	1,200– 4,000	5,000– 24,000
	Osage	4,800	15,000
	Adams Pool	4,000	34,000
	Wilzetta	4,200	28,000
	Cromwell	3,500	21,000
	Barton Arch	3,200– 3,800	18,000– 20,000
New Mexico	Eunice	3,900	29,000
	Hardy	3,800	28,000
	Hobbs	4,200	30,000
	Jal	3,400	28,000
	Monument	3,900	27,000
Louisiana	Pine Island	1,700	6,600
	Evangeline	3,100– 7,800	31,000– 95,000
	Cotton Valley	8,600	115,000
	Des Allemands	8,500	82,000
	Anse La Butte	4,800– 8,000	26,000– 48,000
	Hackberry	8,100– 9,600	65,000– 82,000
	Lafitte	9,400–10,400	85,000–105,000
	Golden Meadow	5,180–11,160	40,000–110,000
	Leeville (Cap)	3,450– 4,925	22,000– 28,000
	do. (Flank)	6,900– 9,200	60,000– 70,000
Texas	Coleman County	2,400	16,000
	Cayuga	4,100	21,000
	Barbers Hill	3,900	26,000

WELL COSTS (*Continued*)

Field	Depth Range (Feet)	Cost Range (Dollars)
Texas (*Continued*)		
Cedar Lake	4,700	34,000
Cowden	4,300– 5,300	25,000– 37,000
East Texas	3,600	9,500
Hastings	5,500– 6,100	26,000– 29,000
Hendricks	3,000	17,000
Fairbanks	6,900	26,000
K. M. A.	3,800	22,000
Luby	4,300– 5,100	18,000– 22,000
Long Lake	5,300	37,000
McCamey	2,100	14,000
Old Ocean	10,000–11,000	92,000
Slaughter Pool	5,000	26,000– 31,000
Spindletop	3,000– 3,700	32,000
South Houston	4,800	28,000
Panhandle areas	3,000– 3,300	16,000
Tomball	5,600	25,000
Turtle Bay (Land)	6,600	28,000
do. (Water)	do.	40,000
West Beaumont	5,400	24,000
Yates	1,400	10,000
California		
Buena Vista	3,500	22,000
Canal	8,200	65,000
Coles Levee	8,400– 9,500	88,000– 98,000
East Coalinga	7,200– 7,600	85,000
Elwood	3,500	30,000
Dominguez	4,200– 8,500	49,000– 79,000
Kettleman Hills	8,000	120,000
do. (Eocene)	11,000	175,000
Midway	900– 2,000	12,000– 18,000
Paloma	10,500	120,000
Poso Creek	2,700	21,000
Round Mountain	1,800	15,000
Santa Maria	4,500	35,000
Ten Section	8,400	65,000
Ventura	5,700– 9,500	50,000–117,000
Wilmington (Ranger)	3,000	37,000
do. (Terminal)	4,100	52,000
do. (Ford)	5,500	59,500
Rocky Mountains		
Salt Creek	4,000	58,000
Mahoney Dome	4,500	60,000
Illinois	3,000	16,000
Michigan	3,000	14,000

Well spacing determines the number of wells drilled in a property, and the spacing pattern depends, in turn, on a number of factors that are not well known during the early life of a field. Properties which are already fully drilled present no problem, but those which are yet to be developed require consideration of this feature because the future profits will be controlled by the extent to which the number of wells and their distribution achieves recovery of the maximum amount of profitable oil. Locations 330 feet from the property line and 660 feet distant from each other provide 10-acre spacing. Various patterns are used for 20-acre and 40-acre spacing and for five wells to 160 acres. In some western Texas areas where the land unit is the labor of 177 acres a well is placed at each corner and a 5-spot location at the center.

For the appraiser, a study of the nearby fields, and of those fields where the underground conditions resemble the field being examined, will indicate the most practicable and likely spacing program. The form of well spacing which will lead to the greatest ultimate oil recoveries may be quite different from that which serves best the interests of the lessee. The lessee seeks profits and therefore wishes to drill only those wells which add to his profits. Similarly, in fact, the drilling pattern which a lessee desires and wishes to follow may be widely different from that which is required as a matter of practical necessity by reason of the common field-acreage spacing, the offset and competitive wells, and the specific lease requirements and obligations.

Increased density of wells is promoted both by a reduction in drilling costs and by ownership of lands in small tracts when they are held by many lessees. Town-lot drilling is never conducive to orderly and well-considered field development. The west Texas and New Mexico region is illustrative; some areas are drilled with a 40-acre spacing, and others have a well to each 10 acres. The former spacing will probably not yield as much oil as the latter spacing, but it is expected that the lessees' profits will be greater, will be realized earlier, and with less severe demands for investment requirements. The 40-acre spacing probably will provide a lower ultimate return to the landowners, and what he does obtain will be strung out and deferred over a longer period. Where the conditions are such that a slow withdrawal rate permits water drive to be fully effective, thus not only increasing the ultimate amount of oil obtained but also bringing out a greater portion of it under flowing conditions instead of by pumping, a wider spacing of wells is probably warranted.

The appraiser may properly inquire about, and take account of, the readiness with which permits to drill are to be obtained and the costs of the permits in states where the administrative bodies control the privilege.

Operating Costs. These costs constitute the field operations that are concerned with bringing out the oil and gas and with their care and disposal at the surface.

Sometimes the heading is divided into " direct " or actual lifting costs at the property (labor, power and fuel, repairs, renewals) and into the field organization expenses which, in turn, are distributed over a number of property units on some ratable basis (supervision, engineering, accounting, timekeeping, warehousing, general transportation). Many company accounts also contain a " G.F.E." (General Field Expense) record, in which are placed the charges for the general benefit of all the properties within a field or district, but which do not fall clearly into any specific subdivision. This account usually becomes a dumping ground not only for charges which are not readily classified but also for those charges which are desired to be buried from view.

The relation of costs to income, as derived in various forms in the many different kinds of operating records, is built around the essential features listed on page 116.

In the determination of a proper measure of production costs for use in estimates, two courses are open to the appraiser. In the first course he ascertains the definite record of the property under consideration, or he draws on his experience elsewhere with similar properties for his yardstick of costs, expressed in terms of well operating units and not of costs per barrel. The field cost of operating any given well is little different, within reasonable limits, whether the amount of oil pumped is great or small. The pumping assembly which is installed for pumping an 80-barrel well continues in use when the well has declined to less than half that rate, but the cost of the operation continues practically unchanged.

The other class of situations is found where either the wells have not as yet been drilled or where for various reasons the operating records are not available, and it is desired to turn to some fixed unit cost, expressed per barrel of oil. This course is sound, but frequently it does result in the adoption of a unit that is on the low side, especially when applied to estimates of future profits where the decline of production rate is in an erratic downward trend. It is possible to counter this tendency toward exaggerated profit estimates by introducing assumptions of advancing costs, but they are uncertain and the method is cumbersome. This objection has less force when the production rates are so severely restricted that they are expected to continue at a uniform pace over a considerable period of years. Once the rate of withdrawal is established in the estimate, the costs on either a well or

ANDOR OIL COMPANY

Operating Record

District_____

Lease_____

Production

OIL	Gross sales	barrels			
	Royalty	do.			
	Net sales	do.			
	Amount @ $	per barrel			$
GAS	Gross sales	mcf			
	Amount @ $	per mcf	$		
	Royalty		$		
	Net sales				$
GASOLINE	Gross sales	gallons			
	Amount @ $	per gallon	$		
	Royalty		$		
	Net sales				$

Total revenue from net production　　　　　$

Costs

Field production　　　　　$

Field general　　　　　$

Total field controllable expenses　　　　　$

Operating profit　　　　　$

Overhead — Administration, etc.　　　　　$

　　　Taxes and insurance　　　　　$

Total overhead　　　　　$

Net profit after operating and overhead expenses　　　　　$

a per-barrel basis may be applied and the only other important element is the point in time when the well is expected to cease flowing and to be put on the beam.

However, the most desirable cost unit, and one that is conclusive if it can be ascertained, is the actually recorded experience at the property, subject to such modifications as may appear warranted by circumstances observed by the appraiser.

Operating costs per well range from amounts which are almost insignificant up to $600 or more per well-month, the latter rate being found where heavy equipment handles a considerable volume of water with the oil and where the repair charges are high. A shallow well, with 2-inch tubing and with light rods operated from a jackpower under slow motion and which pumps off so that many wells are driven from the one power, is operated for $30 per well-month in company operation and for substantially less by the individual operator who is not so strictly controlled in matters of wages and hours of employment. Many farms throughout the eastern United States contain wells which yield less than a half barrel per day; their profitable operation is possible only by the fact that repair expenses are negligible and the men who milk the cows also attend the wells. Wells which require more attention, where a smaller number of wells can be attached to each power, require $50 to $90 per well-month. Small, individually pumped wells ranging from 2,800 to 3,500 feet in depth require $100 to $150 per well-month. Wells which handle greater amounts of fluid and require frequent repairs and cleaning out will demand $2,000 to $7,000 and more per well-year. Of course, this last figure is excessive, but it is not unknown where the depths are more than 5,000 feet, with large volumes of fluid to be handled and the greatest possible immediate recovery the goal. High well costs generally prevail at properties where curtailment and restriction of production are ignored.

However, it does not follow that a minimum of repairs and a high percentage of time-operation promote efficiency. A slow pumping motion and a short stroke are conducive to low costs and to few shut-downs for repairs; this combination supplies an appearance of efficiency. In many competitive situations where the obvious objective is early oil recoveries, an increased speed with the pitman out in the third hole will procure increased amounts of oil and more than compensate for the greater repair costs and the time losses through shutdowns.

Cost per barrel is the unit that has economic significance. It is comparable to price and profit, is readily considered, and so receives most of the attention. A stripper well which costs $20 per month to operate and yields 15 barrels per month has a barrel cost which places it in the marginal class. Many stripper wells belong to the small owner-operators; when the price of crude is up, they make wages or better; when it is down, they lose something.

Conditions of low costs per barrel for operations are illustrated by such fields as Augusta and Eldorado, Kansas, and Wortham, Texas, where the major portions of all the oil produced from wells were obtained during the first year; and the more recent fields of the type of East Texas, Yates, and Hobbs, where the oil is withdrawn by low flowing rates over a long period. In the former group the oil was brought out in a hurry, under emergency need and the high prices which followed World War 1. The latter group represents the attempts to fit supply to demand in a production practice which spreads the recovery over a much longer period, probably obtains more oil from the reservoir, and for the individual producer may be less desirable by reason of deferment of earnings, even though beneficial to the industry when considered as an economic group.

The actual lifting expenses for this class of production are trivial, provided the work is on a sufficient scale to spread out the inescapable costs of watching the wells and of gauging and running the oil. A property which has only three wells and requires an individual caretaker will incur a labor cost four times per barrel that of a similarly situated property which has twelve wells.

Under the present-day requirements for field accounting and restrictions on work conditions it is difficult in the most favorable circumstances to have a field operating expense of less than 4 cents per barrel. From 6 to 10 cents is a more common experience where the conditions are favorable and most of the wells still flow. The outlays for labor, repairs, and power increase when the wells are put to pumping. With a pumping cost of 15 cents per barrel the average distribution is about as follows.

Supervision	$0.01
Labor	0.08
Fuel and power	0.02
Repairs	0.03
Treatment and delivery	0.01
	$0.15

On the West Coast the average labor costs per barrel will be found to be less, the fuel and power costs greater, and the general average a cent or two below comparable costs in the eastern fields. The individually pumped heavy units, where the sands are loose and caving and tend to come into the hole, have higher costs especially if the caving sand has not been fought out and either a cavity of fair size established back of the pipe or else some form of gravel pack or its equivalent inserted.

Individual pumping units have flexibility and mobility; they are independent of the roughness of the ground and they can handle large volumes of water. They are now to be had in a wide range of power capacities, and cost from about $350 per horsepower in the small sizes of about 3 horsepower to $150 per horsepower in the larger units which are built to 35 horsepower.

Grouped pumping through the medium of the jackpower and rod-line plant is, of course, the means of low-cost operation of shallow wells, where the wells are in sufficient number to distribute the initial cost, because of the mechanical efficiency and cheap maintenance. Conditions are best where the terrain is flat and the plant so situated that the load can be balanced, and with the rod lines not over a half mile in length. Increased costs result from scattered and unevenly distributed tracts of small size, roads to cross, rough topography, and long rod lines.

Gas lift or *air lift* as a means of bringing out the oil is of questionable benefit during the early life of a field; it is yet to be shown that an increased ultimate production results. An earlier withdrawal of the oil is effected with a capture of additional oil from the neighbor, provided he does not follow along with a similar expedited withdrawal, and possibly a reduction in the total overall cost. However, this reduction has not been an invariable experience.

Seminole is a splendid example of so-called operating efficiency, in the form of gas and air lift, that flooded the market with new supplies of oil to such an extent that the price was broken. In the long run the producers were affected adversely because the decreased revenue more than offset the reduced costs and earlier recoveries of oil.

Gas-lift installations cost $8,000 to $20,000 for plant, pipe lines, and well equipment. From 1 to 7 mcf of gas are required to raise a barrel of oil. Costs per barrel produced are 6 to 15 cents.

Power costs are largely functions of the utility rates. The monthly power bill for electric motor pumping is $7.00 per horsepower with electricity at 1 cent per kilowatthour; $14.00 when the rate is 2 cents; $20.00 when it is 3 cents.

Monthly gas costs for a gas engine are $0.70 per horsepower when the gas rate is 5 cents per thousand cubic feet; $1.35 when it is 10 cents; $2.00 when it is 15 cents.

Monthly gas cost for boiler and engine in field operations is $2.40 per horsepower with gas at 5 cents, and in that proportion with increased gas rates.

Miscellaneous expenses, it should be noted, arise from the many devices, tools, methods, and processes relating to production practices which are patented and whose use is restricted to licensees. Many specialized technical services are founded on patent control, such as logging, coring, directional drilling, cementing, acidizing, gun perforating. The total amount spent for them in the course of a year may run to a considerable sum in certain types of operations.

Certain production costs increase as the wells grow older. The dehydration of emulsified crude requires treatment which costs from 1½ to 6 cents per barrel of clean oil throughput. The disposal of waste water sometimes requires elaborate and costly arrangements. Taxes of all kinds are a one-way curve.

Occasionally, but usually less often, the costs may be found to decrease for a time, either because of additional well completions over which to spread the fixed charges or because of those changes and economies made necessary by declining production rates and narrowed profit margins.

The December, 1935, report of the United States Petroleum Administrative Board contains material condensed from the answers to a widely circulated questionnaire. From it the following record of reported " Operating Costs and General Overhead Expense " provides an indication of the relative costs per barrel in the various areas.

	Field	Costs per Gross Barrel Operations	General Overhead
California	Los Angeles Basin	$0.226	$0.160
	Coastal	0.146	0.168
	San Joaquin Valley	0.224	0.152
Texas	Panhandle	0.216	0.242
	West Texas	0.114	0.207
	North Texas	0.333	0.220
	Central Texas	0.238	0.160
	Southwest Texas	0.161	0.160
	Gulf Coast	0.155	0.211
Oklahoma	Burbank	0.274	0.260
	Cushing	0.332	0.281
	Seminole	0.166	0.306
Louisiana	Northwest	0.201	0.226
	Gulf Coast	0.384	0.183
Kansas		0.210	0.230
Arkansas		0.405	0.178
New Mexico		0.077	0.282
Wyoming		0.323	0.153
Kentucky		0.312	0.206
Pennsylvania		0.530	0.189

War-time conditions have brought many changes to these cost units, but for purposes of comparison of one field with another they are a sufficiently satisfactory guide.

TAXES

They occur in many forms; none is acceptable, but they must be taken into account with great care in any realistic valuation of producing oil properties. Tax increases during recent years have been at a greater rate than any other cost item, with the possible exceptions of legal and accounting items. For a long time the oil producer paid

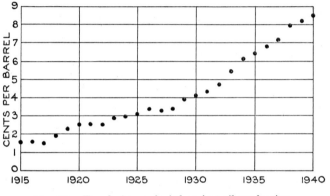

FIG. 30.   Trend of taxes levied against oil production.

a total tax that was equivalent to about 1½ cents per barrel produced. Then came increased levies in various forms, without uniformity in the several states, and now the average tax costs have grown to about 9 cents per barrel produced, not including the iniquitous income taxes. Figure 30 records the advances of the past twenty-five years.

But a high tax is no new thing.   Professor Wright in his *Oil Regions of Pennsylvania* (1865) relates

> The newly imposed tax of one dollar per barrel laid by the general government on crude oil is a subject of much complaint, not only on account of its pecuniary weight, but for the other annoyances in connection with it.   One of these will doubtless be the frequent exercise of that rule known as " reduction descending " in regard to the reported yield of many wells.

Forms of taxes applied in different states are on page 122.   Not every form is in each state.   The most important are those of ad valorem, severance, and income.

FORMS OF TAXES

Capital stock
Franchise
Privilege
Ad valorem
Use
Stream pollution
Federal property transfer stamp tax

Unemployment (social security)
Severance or gross production
Income
School
Sales
Proration

When specific inquiry cannot be made, it is wise to assume 9 cents per net barrel produced as a probable measure of all tax charges except those of state and federal income. In states where the gross-production tax rate exceeds 2½ per cent the fixed total is generally higher than the 9-cent rate referred to; and generally those states having high gross-production taxes have higher total rates than the others. Taxes differ in nearby counties as well as in states, and are quite unpredictable and beyond explanation. The engineer must disengage himself from an idea that they lend themselves to analysis or are based upon reasonable considerations of equity. As Jud Hillman said when in Kentucky, " they are out of need by political expediency."

The *gross-production tax* or *severance* contemplates a levy placed on the removal of minerals from the ground, and during its early years it was considered, at least in theory, to be in lieu of all other taxes, especially those of an ad valorem nature. It has long since ceased to have that limitation and, with the insidious stealth of a bad habit, has expanded in extent and variety to many new forms and applications.

Canadian taxes are not uniform in the provinces. Alberta is representative fairly of the others and contains the most important oil and gas properties.

The registration fee is $130 for a company with a capital of $100,-000; $370 for one with a capital of $500,000. Companies operating natural-gas processing plants pay 2½ per cent of the taxable income or $10,000, whichever is greater. The pipe-line tax is a charge of 10 mills on the dollar of assessed valuation of the pipe line, including the casing in any well to which the pipe line is connected.

TAXES LEVIED AGAINST OIL AND GAS PRODUCED

(Gross Production, Severance, Stream Pollution, Proration, Privilege, License, School, Gross Sales, or Gross Income)

Alabama   2% of the gross casinghead value of oil and gas. (S. B. 364, Laws of 1939, approved July 10, 1940.)

Arizona	1% of the value, the gross proceeds, or the gross incomes from oil or natural gas. (Emergency Revenue Act of 1933, as amended by the Excise Revenue Act of 1935, Section 2c 1.)
Arkansas	2½% of the gross cash market value of the oil and gas produced. (Section 13371, Pope's 1937 *Digest*.)
	$\frac{1}{10}$ of 1% additional tax. (Section 13393.)
	Also, the oil and gas commission is authorized to assess a charge of not over ½ cent per barrel or oil and ½ mill per thousand cubic feet of gas produced and saved. (Act 105, Laws of 1939.)
California	To cover administration of the division of oil and gas, a levy not to exceed $275,000 annually. This amounts to about 1.0 mill per barrel of oil produced and 1.0 mill per 10 mcf gas sold. (Sections 3411, 3402, and 3403, Chapter 93, Laws of 1939.)
Illinois	3% of the value of oil and gas.
Indiana	¼ of 1% of the gross income from oil and natural gas. (Chapter 50, Laws of 1933.)
Kansas	$\frac{1}{25}$ of 1 cent per barrel of oil, imposed by State Board of Health.
	$\frac{1}{10}$ of 1 cent per barrel of oil, imposed by State Corporation Commission.
	½ mill per thousand cubic feet of gas produced, sold, marketed or used. (Chapter 85, Laws of 1933.)
Kentucky	½ of 1% of the market value of crude oil produced.
	In addition, any county may impose a tax of not over 1% of the market value of crude oil produced in the county, for road, county, or school purposes. (Section 4223c 1.)
Louisiana	6 ¢ per barrel on oil of 22° gravity and below.
	7 ¢ do. oil above 22° gravity and not above 28°.
	7½¢ do. oil above 28° do. 31°.
	8 ¢ do. oil above 31° do. 32°.
	9½¢ do. oil above 32° do. 36°.
	10½¢ do. oil above 36° do. 43°.
	11 ¢ do. oil above 43°
	11 ¢ do. distillate, condensate or similar natural resources (not including natural gasoline).
	1 ¢ per barrel on natural gasoline.
	$\frac{3}{10}$ of 1 cent per thousand cubic feet of gas at 10-ounce pressure. (Act 145, 1940.)
	½ cent per thousand cubic feet of gas " gathered." (Act 153, 1940.)
Michigan	2% of the gross cash market value of oil and gas. (Section 3606.)
	⅜ of 1 cent per barrel privilege fee. (Act 61, 1939.)
Mississippi	2% of the sale value of oil.
	2½% of sale value of natural gas. (Chapter 161A, 1938.)
Montana	2% of the gross value of petroleum. (Chapter 217, Section 2398, 1935.)
	¼ of 1 cent per barrel privilege or license tax. (Chapter 123, 1935.)
	Also, a " net proceeds " tax based on the gross value of oil and natural gas, with certain deductions for costs, etc. The rate is equal to the state and county ad valoreum tax rates. (Chapter 189, Section 2090, 1935.)

New Mexico   2% of value of oil and gas. (Section 9704A102, 1938 Supplement.)
2% additional of gross receipts from oil and gas. (Chapter 192, 1937.)
⅛ of 1% of proceeds from oil and gas. (Section 97–825, 1938.)
Also, a general property tax for the district where the property is situated, based on the value of the production less 50% credit for amortization and lifting cost. (Chapter 97, Section 97–402, 1929.)

Oklahoma   5% of the gross value of petroleum and natural gas. (H. B. 87, 1935.)
12½% of gross value of oil recovered from streams, waters, natural depressions into which it has escaped and where the actual source is not disclosed. (Chapter 103, 1933.)
⅛ of 1 cent per barrel, for the collection of gross production tax. (H. B. 135, 1939.)

Oregon   ½ cent per barrel marketed. (Section 53–310.)

Texas   5.2% of market value of natural gas, including casinghead gas, 4¾ cents per barrel on oil produced; but if the market value of the oil exceeds $1.00 per barrel, then the rate is 4⅜%. (House Bill 8, 1941, effective May 1, 1941.)
$\frac{3}{16}$ of 1 cent per barrel for proration. (1936.)

Washington   ¼ of 1% of the value of oil and natural gas. (Chapter 180, 1935.)

West Virginia   3.9% of gross proceeds from oil.
7.8% of gross proceeds from natural gas over $5,000. (Chapter 11, Article 13.)

Canada   Alberta provincial royalty tax of 10% of gross production of crude or naphtha, and 5% on natural gasoline recovered by absorption process in amounts of ½ gallon per mcf. The rate increases on a sliding scale with greater recoveries.

Income Taxes. This creature first reared its ugly head in 1913, but was no great burden during the ensuing few years. After the year 1917, it gradually became more oppressive, and is now of consequence in any valuation that is based on or gives weight to prospective earnings and profits. Income taxes differ in their effect as to ownership, whether in a corporation or privately held, with the advantage in personal ownership of avoiding the additional corporation tax. The influence of depreciation and depletion allowances in the computation of taxable income is important.

The effect of income taxes, accordingly, on a property valuation is largely controlled by the purpose of the valuation. If it is aimed at the worth to an individual owner, then the owner's personal income tax position as to surtax brackets is important. The value to a corporation is affected by that portion of the total income tax paid by the company that is properly chargeable to this unit of property. Any single property which is company owned, has all its wells drilled, and is considered as an entity and not in relation to an entire corporation tax situation, is faced with a current federal income tax liability of not less than 25 per cent of the net cash operating profits, unless modified by cost depletion. In individual ownership, the minimum rate against future cash profits in estimating the net return when cost depletion does not apply should be 65 per cent of the top-bracket rate paid by the individual.

1940 STATE CORPORATION INCOME TAX RATES, ON INCOME FROM PROPERTY AND/OR INTANGIBLE ASSETS IN THE STATE

Alabama	3 %	of net income
Arizona	5 %	do. (if over $7,000, the rates range from 1% for the first $1,000 to 5% in excess of $6,000)
Arkansas	2 %	do.
California	4 %	do.
Colorado	4 %	do.
Connecticut	2 %	do.
District of Columbia	5 %	do.
Georgia	5½%	do.
Idaho	8 %	of net income over $5,000. 1½% for net income below that
Indiana	1 %	of gross income
Iowa	2 %	of net income
Kansas	2 %	do.
Kentucky	4 %	do.
Louisiana	4 %	do.
Maryland	1½%	do.
Massachusetts	2½%	of net income plus 15% of tax in 1939 and 10% of tax for 1940
Minnesota	6 %	of net income
Mississippi	8 %	of net income over $10,000. Below that it varies from 3% to 7%
Missouri	2 %	of net income
Montana	3 %	do.
New Mexico	2 %	do.
New York	6 %	do.
North Carolina	6 %	do.
North Dakota	6 %	of net income over $15,000. Below that it varies from 3% to 5%
Oklahoma	6 %	of net income
Oregon	8 %	do.
Pennsylvania	7 %	do.
South Carolina	4½%	do.
South Dakota		various, from 1% to 8%
Tennessee	3¾%	of net income
Utah	3 %	do.
Vermont	2 %	do.
Virginia	3 %	do.
Washington		0.0025 of value of products or gross sales
Wisconsin	6 %	of net income over $6,000. Below that it varies from 2% to 5%

Valuations are occasionally required " as of " a specific date in the past. The following table contains the federal income tax rates since 1913. If the specific date falls during the period from 1918 until 1926 when the Revenue Act of 1918 was in effect, and if discoveries of new supplies of crude were made at the property during that time, then consideration should be given to the influence of allowable " discovery values " in the depletion account which is set up against income in determining the net taxable income.

FEDERAL CORPORATION INCOME TAX RATES

Year	Percentage of Taxable Income			
1913, 14, 15	1 %			
1916	2 %			
1917	4 %			
1918	12 %	Also excess profits tax		
1919, 20	10 %			
1921	10 %			
1922, 23, 24	12½%			
1925	13 %			
1926, 27	13½%			
1928, 29, 30, 31	12 %			
1932, 33, 34	13¾%			
1935	12½%	of net income	up to $ 2,000	Also excess profits tax
	13 %	do.	from $ 2,000–$15,000	
	14 %	do.	from $15,000–$40,000	
	15 %	do.	above $40,000	
1936, 37	8 %	do.	up to $ 2,000	
	11 %	do.	from $ 2,000–$15,000	Also excess profits tax
	13 %	do.	from $15,000–$40,000	
	15 %	do.	above $40,000	
1938	19 %			Also excess profits tax
1939	19 %	or 16½% if all earnings distributed		
1940	19 %	do.		
1941	24 %	of net income		
	31 %	do.		

The 1941 Canadian Dominion corporation income tax is 18 per cent on net taxable income, together with excess profits tax of either 12 per cent or 75 per cent, whichever is the higher of the methods by which the government permits the figures. The lowest rate permitted is 30 per cent. In determining income of oil properties, depreciation of preproduction costs may be written off at progressive rates for five years of 30 per cent, 20 per cent, 15 per cent, 12 per cent, and 10 per cent. Depletion is permitted at the rate of 25 per cent of net profits from production after allowance of development and depreciation charges. Depletion is allowed as long as production continues, but only against production income and not against such sources as interest, rentals, and other investment income. Exploration and dry holes are permitted to be charged off in the year incurred, except that exploration costs at properties substantially removed from the producing wells may not be so charged. Alberta has a provincial income tax, in addition, of 5 per cent of the taxable income.

Administration and Supervision. Under this heading are charged direction, executives, central office expense, accounting, insurance, supervision, personnel relations, public relations. Together with the taxes they are designated as *overhead,* in distinction from the field controllable expenses. In many company records the charges vary widely, both by reason of management ability and the differences in accounting methods, and this is especially true with the smaller companies where a single unusual salary may affect the earnings to the extent of several cents per barrel. Sometimes such central office costs as rents, office and clerical expenses, supervision, and other salaries are made to appear low by the expedient of allocating portions of them directly against field departmental headings. This disturbs the field superintendent and renders his own controllable costs records useless to him.

From 4 to 7 cents per net barrel of oil produced is a good general measure of the genuine administration costs for producing oil from developed properties. It includes about ½ cent for insurance, but does not cover those office and supervisory charges incurred for the benefit of an expansion program directed toward exploration for new properties and their acquisition. Such activities require geologists, draftsmen, land men, scouts, title examiners, etc., whose salaries (and expense accounts) are usually charged in the general overhead of the central office.

Among those conditions which contribute to high overhead rates, in addition to the occasional unexplainable top salaries, are scattered and unbalanced properties, costly partnership interests, litigation, operations conducted under exacting governmental supervision. Taking into account a reasonable proportion of such undesirable operating conditions, together with a healthy activity and effort to find new oil sources so that the reserves may be maintained in a ratio of not less than 5,000 barrels of proved oil for each daily barrel of current production rate, the combined administration and supervision and central office expense will range between 18 and 26 cents per net barrel produced. This item is pertinent only when the general outlook for company earnings is under consideration and not when the question is that of the value of a specific single property or of a group of producing properties.

Present Worth of Future Earnings

Hoskold introduced into mine valuations the use of the discount element of " present worth " as a factor. The theory has its origin in the conception that the present value of future income or earnings should be expressed by applying a suitable discount. In oil-field appraisal practice it received attention in 1915 from the Appraisement Committee of the Independent Oil Producers' Agency, which outlined the four steps in computing the value of an oil property as

1. The estimate of future working costs
2. The estimated annual receipts
3. The present value of each year's net profits, discounted at 8 per cent
4. The salvage value of the excess equipment

Since then the use of the discount factor has been widely adopted, with the obvious and simple objective at the beginning of bringing to today's value the earnings or income expected through the future years. But its application has wandered off into curious forms, through the efforts to blend into a single discount rate two quite diverse factors: (1) the measurable interest value of money; (2) the uncertainties and hazards connected with the prediction of well behaviors and their production capacities, and more recently the further fogs of restricted production rates and statutory control of output. Differences of opinion as to the nature and extent of the discount factor and the manner in which it should be employed have led to the one view that high discount rates are justified because of the uncertainties in the business and the " hazardous " nature of oil wells; whereas the other considers discount as an interest factor only, representing a price paid for the use of money. The latter approach appears to be the more logically appropriate.

Among the reasons for the high regard in which the discount factor is held are the facts that it is positive and definite; it can be mathematically justified; it is sound as to those mining deposits which can be seen and measured (generally with a nicety that is never possible for oil reserves). It has attained a place in that procedure, designated by some one having a flair for descriptive fancy, as " scientific accounting."

Present worth is the principal amount less the compound discount.

Compound discount is the difference between the principal amount and its present worth. The formula for computing this is

$$\text{Compound discount} = 1 - \frac{1}{\left(1 + \dfrac{r}{i}\right)^{p}}$$

where r = interest rate
   i = interest conversions per year
   p = interest conversions during entire period.

Thus, if the compound discount is desired on a principal amount of $5,000, due 8 years hence, with interest at the rate of 6 per cent annually and compounded semi-annually, the present worth factor is

$$\frac{1}{\left(1 + \dfrac{0.06}{2}\right)^{15}} = \frac{1}{(1.03)^{15}}$$

$$= 0.642$$

$$\$5000 \times 0.642 = \$3,210$$

In Table I are the factors for various rates of interest, based upon the amounts being received throughout the year and with the interest compounded semi-annually. The time, accordingly, with the

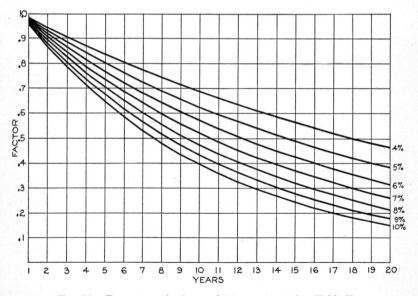

Fig. 31. Present worth of annual future returns (see Table I).

receipts from the sale of oil spread uniformly over the year is expressed as equivalent to a middle point in the year, or $(2n - 1)/2$ as to any given yearly period. The data contained in Table I are also presented in graphic form in Fig. 31. The application of these discounts in the conventional forms of engineering appraisals is taken up in Chapter VI.

TABLE I

PRESENT WORTH OF $1.00 PRINCIPAL AMOUNT TO BE RECEIVED AT $(2n - 1)/2$ YEARS.
INTEREST CONVERTED SEMI-ANNUALLY

Year	4%	5%	6%	7%	8%	9%	10%	Year
1	0.980	0.976	0.971	0.966	0.961	0.957	0.952	1
2	0.942	0.929	0.915	0.902	0.889	0.876	0.864	2
3	0.906	0.884	0.863	0.842	0.822	0.802	0.783	3
4	0.871	0.841	0.813	0.786	0.760	0.735	0.711	4
5	0.837	0.801	0.766	0.734	0.703	0.673	0.645	5
6	0.804	0.762	0.722	0.685	0.650	0.616	0.585	6
7	0.773	0.725	0.681	0.639	0.601	0.564	0.530	7
8	0.743	0.690	0.642	0.597	0.555	0.517	0.481	8
9	0.714	0.657	0.605	0.557	0.513	0.473	0.436	9
10	0.686	0.626	0.570	0.520	0.475	0.433	0.396	10
11	0.660	0.595	0.537	0.486	0.439	0.397	0.359	11
12	0.634	0.567	0.507	0.453	0.406	0.363	0.326	12
13	0.610	0.539	0.478	0.423	0.375	0.333	0.295	13
14	0.586	0.513	0.450	0.395	0.347	0.305	0.268	14
15	0.563	0.489	0.424	0.369	0.321	0.279	0.243	15
16	0.541	0.465	0.400	0.344	0.297	0.255	0.220	16
17	0.520	0.443	0.377	0.321	0.274	0.234	0.200	17
18	0.500	0.421	0.355	0.300	0.253	0.214	0.181	18
19	0.481	0.401	0.335	0.280	0.234	0.196	0.164	19
20	0.462	0.382	0.316	0.261	0.217	0.180	0.149	20
21	0.444	0.363	0.298	0.244	0.200	0.165	0.135	21
22	0.427	0.346	0.281	0.228	0.185	0.151	0.123	22
23	0.410	0.329	0.264	0.213	0.171	0.138	0.111	23
24	0.394	0.313	0.249	0.199	0.158	0.126	0.101	24
25	0.379	0.298	0.235	0.185	0.146	0.116	0.092	25

It often happens that the total estimated profits to be derived from a property is computed to a fairly satisfactory degree, but that the rate at which the profits will become available cannot be outlined more closely than a general conclusion that the total amount will be received in equal instalments over some given period of time. Table II contains the present-worth factors for this requirement. Thus, if a net profit of $10,000 is to be received in equal instalments over a period of

TABLE II

PRESENT WORTH OF $1.00 TO BE RECEIVED IN EQUAL INSTALMENTS OVER
VARYING PERIODS. INTEREST CONVERTED SEMI-ANNUALLY

Year	4%	5%	6%	7%	8%	9%	10%	Year
1	0.980	0.976	0.971	0.966	0.961	0.957	0.952	1
2	0.961	0.952	0.943	0.934	0.925	0.916	0.908	2
3	0.943	0.930	0.916	0.903	0.891	0.878	0.866	3
4	0.927	0.907	0.890	0.874	0.858	0.842	0.828	4
5	0.907	0.886	0.866	0.846	0.827	0.809	0.791	5
6	0.890	0.865	0.842	0.819	0.797	0.777	0.757	6
7	0.873	0.845	0.819	0.793	0.770	0.746	0.724	7
8	0.857	0.826	0.797	0.769	0.743	0.718	0.694	8
9	0.840	0.808	0.775	0.745	0.717	0.690	0.665	9
10	0.825	0.789	0.755	0.723	0.693	0.665	0.638	10
11	0.810	0.771	0.744	0.701	0.670	0.640	0.613	11
12	0.796	0.754	0.724	0.681	0.648	0.617	0.589	12
13	0.783	0.738	0.705	0.662	0.627	0.596	0.566	13
14	0.768	0.723	0.687	0.643	0.607	0.575	0.545	14
15	0.753	0.706	0.669	0.624	0.588	0.556	0.524	15
16	0.742	0.692	0.653	0.606	0.570	0.537	0.506	16
17	0.728	0.677	0.637	0.590	0.552	0.518	0.488	17
18	0.715	0.663	0.622	0.573	0.536	0.502	0.472	18
19	0.703	0.649	0.607	0.558	0.520	0.486	0.457	19
20	0.691	0.636	0.591	0.543	0.505	0.470	0.439	20
21	0.679	0.623	0.578	0.529	0.491	0.456	0.425	21
22	0.668	0.611	0.565	0.516	0.477	0.442	0.411	22
23	0.657	0.598	0.552	0.503	0.463	0.428	0.398	23
24	0.646	0.586	0.539	0.489	0.451	0.417	0.386	24
25	0.635	0.575	0.527	0.478	0.438	0.403	0.374	25

12 years and is to be discounted at a 5 per cent annual rate, the factor for 5 per cent and 12 years is found to be 0.754. The present value of these future receipts, then, discounted at 5 per cent annually, is $10,000 times 0.754, or $7,540.

Figure 32 shows diagrammatically the data in Table II, and is useful for ascertaining quickly the approximate factors which correspond to various time and interest rate combinations. For example, if payments are expected at about the same rate during a period of 20 years, and the discount to be applied is 6 per cent, then the present-worth factor is about 0.59. This unit is, in fact, a useful one to remember because often the specific timing of future returns is quite unpredictable and a factor of 0.6 is fairly responsive to the vague and indecisive question of the worth today of these future profits, on a theory that an equally spaced 20-year period represents about a reasonable expectation.

Unsettled outlooks as to the timing can be narrowed somewhat by drawing up a schedule which conforms more closely to the expectation than the assumption of equal returns over a given period of years. It may be estimated in a given situation that half of the oil will be

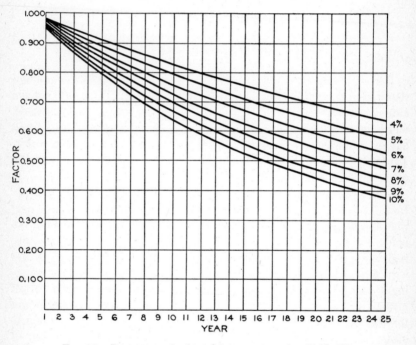

Fig. 32. Present worth of total future return (see Table II).

brought out during the first five years, 25 per cent more during the ensuing 5 years, and the remaining 25 per cent over a long period thereafter. The composite factor for this schedule of returns is obtained by reference to Fig. 31. Assuming that 5 per cent is the adopted rate, the general average of the 5 per cent curve for the years from 1 to 5 is about 0.9; for the years from 6 to 10 it is about 0.7; and for a long but indefinite stretch thereafter it would be 0.45. The correct factor is 0.7375.

$$
\begin{array}{ll}
0.50 \times 0.9 & 0.45 \\
0.25 \times 0.7 & 0.175 \\
0.25 \times 0.45 & 0.1125 \\
\hline
& 0.7375
\end{array}
$$

Or, in an unrestricted production area it might be that the first two years are expected to provide 60 per cent of the total ultimate oil; the next three years 20 per cent more, and the remaining 20 per cent spread out indefinitely. With a 5 per cent rate, the factor is found to be 0.85.

$$0.60 \times 0.95 \quad 0.57$$
$$0.20 \times 0.85 \quad 0.17$$
$$0.20 \times 0.55 \quad 0.11$$
$$\overline{}$$
$$0.85$$

The surplus and salvage equipment found at a property and not required in the normal course of operations and free to be sold have a clear warehouse value. That salvable material, which, it is expected, will be released at some quite distant time when the oil operations will have terminated, has normally a small and negligible present worth. Table III shows the present worth, at varying rates of interest, of $1.00 to be received at the end of future years.

No one prevailing discount rate has received general acceptance. Both 5 per cent and 6 per cent have been commonly used in the past; the present trend is toward lower rates. In general it is in order to point out that the discount factor has gone far afield from simply registering the use of money. It should be used with caution and with a clear understanding of its limitations and the reason for bringing it into a computation. When it represents the amortization of an investment, a return of the capital plus some further amounts paid for the use of the money, it has genuine purpose and place. Quite often, however, a rate of 10 per cent or more is chosen, clearly out of line with the actual cost of money, accompanied with an explanation that this allows for " hazard," " risk," " water hazard," " contingencies," or " conservatism." At other times the 10 per cent may be found without any explanation other than that it is permitted by the Internal Revenue Bureau when used in matters relating to federal gift and inheritance taxes.

In any event, discount factors should not be applied to oil reserves or to estimates of oil recoveries. Nor should they attempt to delineate some form of a profit element, which would be directly contrary to the fundamental conception that the speculations and uncertainties in an engineering report should be confined to as small a field as possible. It is of the utmost importance that the reader of a valuation, especially the client, have fully explained to him what has been done with his future profits, and why. Wiping these out with discount factors, under the guise of a revision in the estimate of future earnings, is not revealing. Discounting is a refinement, and its use for any purpose other than that of expressing the hire of money and the return of capital implies a degree of certainty or of precision that is rarely attained in valuations. Uncertainties as to prices, costs, demand, taxes are too great to permit their being pegged and disposed of with a mathematical factor.

TABLE III

PRESENT VALUE OF $1.00 DUE AT THE END OF EACH YEAR, WITH
INTEREST CONVERTED ANNUALLY

Year	4%	5%	6%	7%
1	0.962	0.952	0.943	0.935
2	0.925	0.907	0.890	0.873
3	0.889	0.864	0.840	0.816
4	0.855	0.823	0.792	0.763
5	0.822	0.784	0.747	0.713
6	0.790	0.746	0.705	0.666
7	0.760	0.711	0.665	0.623
8	0.731	0.677	0.627	0.582
9	0.703	0.645	0.592	0.544
10	0.676	0.614	0.558	0.508
11	0.650	0.585	0.527	0.475
12	0.625	0.557	0.497	0.444
13	0.601	0.530	0.469	0.415
14	0.577	0.505	0.442	0.388
15	0.555	0.481	0.417	0.362
16	0.534	0.458	0.394	0.339
17	0.513	0.436	0.371	0.317
18	0.494	0.415	0.350	0.296
19	0.475	0.396	0.330	0.276
20	0.456	0.377	0.312	0.258
21	0.439	0.359	0.294	0.241
22	0.422	0.342	0.278	0.226
23	0.406	0.326	0.262	0.211
24	0.390	0.310	0.247	0.197
25	0.375	0.296	0.233	0.184

Occasionally the discounting of future income is helpful for comparing the relative values of several properties. Two properties with approximately equal estimated future profits from oil of similar quality may be so situated that the recovery of their oil will require widely different periods of time. Appropriate treatment with discounts brings out the money value of that difference.

A genuine danger which arises when the engineer becomes too familiar with discount factors is the temptation when concerned with a legal or a tax matter to use these factors as a means for warping a valuation in the direction which best serves the client. It is not surprising, therefore, that where market value is concerned the analytical or engineering valuation, based on the discounting of estimated profits, meets with suspicion and increasing disfavor. The cumulative effect of several assumptions and estimates in a continued computation is too forceful and lends itself too readily to manipulation.

Uncertainties and variations are inevitable in the course of appraising oil properties. The effort to take up the slack of these irregularities through the introduction of a discount factor is difficult to justify, no matter how earnest may be the desire to be " safe " or to win approval of a report as conservative. If a water hazard is known to exist or is suspected to be present even though not measurable, or if for any reason an estimate of the oil reserves is considered to be high, then a correction or a description of the uncertainty should be taken up in the oil estimate itself, and not in the estimated profits or in their present worth; certainly not in the application of high discounts to earnings which in fact may never be realized.

It is true that the risk element inherent in an estimate of future profits is great; and it is also true that no discount factor will adequately provide for it, and yet may dangerously disarm a reader. The difficulties which accompany estimates of oil reserves and the unpredictable future provide the inevitable risk which justifies an adequate profit to the oil producer. Fair Market Value (Chapter VI), in that it registers the meeting ground of the willing seller and the willing buyer, takes form out of the measure of these risks by the experienced oil operator. Business men may choose to obtain a professional valuation, and may be guided and influenced by it, but no mathematical factor will foretell where a buyer and seller finally will find their ideas agreeing, to the extent that they hang up their hats and make a deal.

THE UNIT PROJECT

This is essentially a pooling of interests and is in marked contrast with the rugged individualism characteristic of the industry. Teamwork among producers has not been a noteworthy quality, and it is not surprising that cooperative ventures have been uncommon and difficult to arrange.

The simplest form of joint action is the community lease where the landowners, usually in town-lot groups of individually held lots or tracts too small to warrant or permit the drilling of a well on each, combine or pool their holdings in one lease document which they all sign. Provision is made for the division of interest, usually on an areal basis, and for the allocation and payment for the royalty portion of the oil and gas produced.

Similarly, a pooling of the working interests where a number of tracts are separately held by different lessees leads to a unit project. The royalty interests may or may not be included, although as a practical matter it is often impossible to arrange a unit without the approval of these interests. No standard form of unit has come into general adoption. The conflicting interests and ideas held by land-owners, lessees, and the owners of overriding royalties are exceedingly difficult to reconcile, especially because the early life of an oil field is the uncertain period when the least is known about the various conditions which have to do with the extent of the field, the occurrence and the behavior of oil and gas. Sometimes unit areas are restricted to those tracts definitely and conclusively proved to be productive. At other times two classes of lands are recognized: (1) those which are proved productive, and (2) an additional surrounding belt which is made a part of the project but does not participate in either the benefits or the obligations until its productivity has become established.

The advantages of unitization are obvious. The disadvantages are not so apparent but are no less real because they relate to the business and human relationships. Valuation of any given tract which is in or is to be placed in a unit project requires, in addition to the valuation of the unit project as an entity, a weighing by the appraiser of the increased or diminished quantities of oil to be obtained and of the benefits from the more orderly withdrawal of the oil, the diversification or spreading of the risk, the reduced outlays for development and operations, provided the outlays will be lessened, in fact, by the unit. The law of diminishing returns affects units which are large and bulky and unwieldy, and very often a small tract in the possession of a capable operator can be made to yield much greater returns than if in the unit and, obviously, at the expense of the unit operation.

MARGINAL PROPERTIES

A property which provides only a small profit from its production during periods of average crude prices requires especial attention in an appraisal to the operating methods, costs and the effects of minor crude price changes. Such properties display surprising longevity in the hands of individual operators who give them the careful and attentive treatment necessary for the maximum possible production.

Old properties are often sold for a price equal to the salvage value of the equipment, a dangerous index of value unless the property is known to be run down, improperly operated, and to hold some prospect of response to careful management. The investment never stops with the purchase price because added amounts are put into improvements and rehabilitations. Transfers of this kind of property usually take place during periods of fairly good crude prices. Then when the price level drops, unless the production rate has been substantially built up, the operations fail to pay. By that time the entire invested amount has exceeded the salvage value of the equipment. Equipment of this kind is difficult to sell during depressed periods.

REFERENCES

J. E. Brantly, *Rotary Drilling Handbook,* 1938.

Cost of Producing Crude Petroleum, U. S. Department of the Interior, 1935.

David T. Day and others, *Handbook of the Petroleum Industry,* 1922.

C. M. Nickerson, " Repressuring in Depleted Oil Zones," *Petroleum Development and Technology,* American Institute of Mining and Metallurgical Engineers, 1930.

Randolph Paul, *Federal Estate and Gift Taxation,* 1942.

B. H. Robinson, " Economics of Pumping," *Drilling and Production Practice,* American Petroleum Institute, 1935.

E. E. Rosaire, " Paradox of Exploration Costs," *World Petroleum,* October, 1938.

P. D. Torrey, " Modern Practice in Water-Flooding," *Petroleum Development and Technology,* American Institute of Mining and Metallurgical Engineers, 1930.

Joseph Zaba and W. H. Doherty, *Practical Petroleum Engineers' Handbook,* 1939.

CHAPTER VI

VALUATION METHODS

Compilation of the valuation itself is the next step, after the property has been examined sufficiently to provide a background for study and interpretation of the known facts. It has been seen that the valuation is to be " as of " a specified date, and that the purpose for which it is done guides, very properly and legitimately, the approach to the undertaking and the relative weights to be applied to the various factors which influence the final conclusions.

In a discussion of the factors and methods, it is well to avoid laying down fixed rules of procedure. Even fixed definitions of factors and methods are undesirable because conditions in the oil fields vary so widely from place to place that it is much more important for the appraiser to work toward a clear understanding of the fundamentals and to retain a certain mental flexibility in the use of data, rather than to be bound to one course. Thus, production costs may be expressed in terms of cost per barrel, or of cost per well, or per property; no one cost will fit every situation; each has its proper field.

The fact that the same property may have different values when considered under different circumstances is not an indictment of any particular valuation practice. These differences arise because the expression " value " has little meaning of itself unless combined with some indication of the purpose association. Among such purposes are the following.

For a seller. The requirement may be a genuinely objective and coldly studied job, prepared as a guide for an owner who contemplates offering his property for sale and wishes an independent opinion of what the future holds for this property and the amount it should bring in a sale. But this seldom happens. More often the seller asks for a description of the property in the form of a " report," prepared as a valuation in such form as to be handed to a prospective buyer.

For a buyer. Where an independent and detached study and examination is required by one who contemplates a purchase.

For a lender. Where the value sought is that which relates to the safeguarding of a loan.

For administrative bodies. Required by the Federal Securities and Exchange Commission, or by the several state blue-sky bodies.

For use in legal proceedings. Where testimony on the market value of property as of some specific date is required.

Tax matters. For the determination of the depreciation and depletion allowances in computing taxable income. Also in connection with inheritance taxes and gift taxes.

Mergers of companies. Here the ascertained values may be relative rather than absolute, provided a joint appraisal has been undertaken and if the participants have agreed on certain yardsticks or units of measure that are to be applied equitably to the properties of each. Such proceedings readily acquire the characteristics of negotiations or of horse trades and tend to become battles of wits.

Unit projects. A unit is a form of merger, to the extent that it involves negotiations similar to those just noted. Usually there are many participants. They introduce conflicting views in the course of jockeying around for trading positions, and thereby increase the difficulties incident to working out an essential common meeting ground.

THE ENGINEERING METHOD

This is also known as the analytical method and is the course most popular for computing the value of a producing oil property. It consists of a capitalization of the estimated future earnings, in the form of the profits which will be derived from the production and sale of the oil and gas. The three fundamentals are the estimates of (1) the recoverable oil and gas; (2) the income to be received from these; (3) the costs of their production and sale. The chief secondary elements are the timing of the production and the discounted present worth of the anticipated profits. In its simplest form, therefore, an engineering valuation is illustrated by the following.

Estimated recoverable oil	2,000,000 gross barrels
Less one-eighth royalty	250,000 barrels
Net oil reserves	1,750,000 net barrels
Estimated income at $1.10 per barrel	$1,925,000
Estimated costs:	
Drill 8 wells at $45,000 $360,000	
Production operations 367,000	727,000
Estimated profits	$1,198,000

This represents a value of the property expressed in terms of its estimated future total earnings, after paying for development and operations, on a cash-in cash-out basis. No additional profit has been added, and no provision has been made for the use of the necessary money advances or for uncertainties.

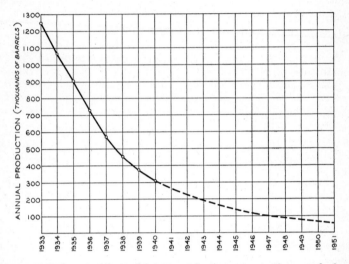

FIG. 33. Relation of estimated future production rates to the record of past production.

The *timing* element is obviously of great consequence. Since this method relies on estimates of future income, it has little field and application if no market exists for the oil or gas. Many valuations of the engineering type have been thoroughly disproved by the unanticipated intervention of curtailment, and by other influences which have affected the demand for crude and the rates of withdrawal. Occasionally production rates are increased over those which have been expected. With all other features equal, that oil which is being produced currently and during the early future is considered the best oil and is worth more than that oil which is to come during a later and more uncertain period. Decline curves which visualize anticipated future production rates lend themselves especially well to the estimates of timing, and they do this most effectively for the wells which have been operated to capacity and free of severe restrictions. The conditions of maximum production rates which have provided this ideal means for a timing schedule obtained widely prior to 1928–30. Capacity wells are now a minority, in importance if not in number.

Figure 33 shows the production rates from a property during recent years. It has 26 pumping wells, which have been operated to capacity since 1928; the oil sells for $0.85 per barrel, and the gas and gasoline income provide an additional 2 cents per barrel of oil produced. The royalty rate is one-eighth. The field operating expenses at the end of the year 1940 were running at the rate of $6,200 per year, and the allocation of costs for overhead, insurance, land and severance taxes, was equivalent to $0.11 per barrel.

Future production, as indicated by the curve, is

Year	Gross Barrels
1941	260,000
1942	223,000
1943	190,000
1944	160,000
1945	134,000
1946	116,000
1947	100,000
1948	86,000
1949	74,000
1950	64,000
1951	58,000

Income at $0.85 per barrel for oil and $0.02 more for revenue from gas and casinghead gasoline provides a total gross income of $0.87 per barrel. The net return, before deducting for operating charges but after allowing for the costs of overhead, insurance, and taxes, is $0.87 less $0.11, or $0.76 per barrel.

Application of these elements then takes the following form.

ESTIMATED FUTURE PROFITS

Year	Production		Return at $0.76	Operating Costs	Cash Profit
	Gross	Net ($\frac{7}{8}$)			
1941	260,000	227,500	$172,900	$62,000	$110,900
1942	223,000	195,125	148,295	59,000	89,295
1943	190,000	166,250	126,350	56,000	70,350
1944	160,000	140,000	106,400	53,000	53,400
1945	134,000	117,250	89,110	50,000	39,110
1946	116,000	101,500	77,140	50,000	27,140
1947	100,000	87,500	66,500	50,000	16,500
1948	86,000	75,250	57,190	50,000	7,190
1949	74,000	64,750	49,210	50,000	
1950	64,000	56,000	42,560		
1951	58,000	50,750	38,570		

The *economic limit* is indicated in the foregoing example to be reached during the year 1949, and no further profitable production should be expected thereafter, as far as this pattern is concerned. Experience has shown, however, that unless price changes intervene the productive life becomes extended by reason of a slowing down of the decline rate which is brought on through a gradual elimination of the weaker wells (see Fig. 17) and an accompanying reduction in costs. The effect upon the entire picture is not great, the change in the estimated oil reserves being much more than the proportionate increase in estimated future profits; and, in general, the influence on the present value of a property is negligible.

Another refinement which can be introduced but which is generally ignored is the value of the equipment which will be recovered at that time in the future when the operations reach an end. The common experience, however, is that such equipment items as are freed from time to time at abandoned wells are needed for replacement at the wells which remain in operation, and that at the time of final abandonment the utility of most of the salvable material is fairly well gone. Its value, after providing for the expenses incidental to plugging the wells and to removal of machinery is found to be small. In addition, the present worth of this recovery at ten or more years hence brings it down to a still lower amount.

Present worth of the estimated future profits derived from the oil and gas production remains to be taken into account. The applicable discount factors for this purpose have been discussed (page 129), with Table I and Fig. 31. Assuming that an annual rate of 5 per cent is to indicate the worth of money, then the final form of the computation is as follows. It is a convenience to have forms of the kind illustrated below either printed or mimeographed, preferably on a fairly stiff paper which will withstand handling and shuffling, especially when repeated appraisals of the same properties are to be carried out from time to time.

The material contained in this form may be augmented with a map that shows the situation of the property and the improvements on it, together with some accounts of the subsurface geological conditions. Also may be shown some further historical data to supplement the production record, such as past gas-oil ratios, bottom-hole pressures, water content, edgewater behavior, and possibly some comments on the condition of the wells and any noteworthy operating features.

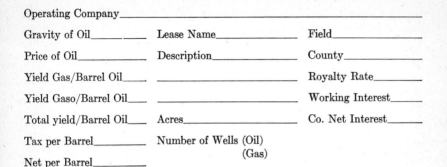

Operating Company_____

Gravity of Oil_____   Lease Name_____   Field_____

Price of Oil_____   Description_____   County_____

Yield Gas/Barrel Oil____   _____   Royalty Rate_____

Yield Gaso/Barrel Oil___   _____   Working Interest_____

Total yield/Barrel Oil___   Acres_____   Co. Net Interest_____

Tax per Barrel_____   Number of Wells (Oil)

Net per Barrel_____   (Gas)

ESTIMATED VALUE OF FUTURE PRODUCTION

Year	Gross Barrels	Co. Net Barrels	Income @ $0.76	Operating Costs	Profit	Discount Factor @ 5%	Present Value
1941	260,000	227,500	$172,900	$62,000	$110,900	0.976	$108,240
1942	223,000	195,125	148,295	59,000	89,295	0.929	82,960
1943	190,000	166,250	126,350	56,000	70,350	0.884	62,190
1944	160,000	140,000	106,400	53,000	53,400	0.841	44,910
1945	134,000	117,250	89,110	50,000	39,110	0.801	31,330
1946	116,000	101,500	77,140	50,000	27,140	0.762	20,680
1947	100,000	87,500	66,500	50,000	16,500	0.725	11,960
1948	86,000	75,250	57,190	50,000	7,190	0.690	4,960
1949	74,000	64,750	49,210	49,210			
	1,343,000	1,175,125	$893,095	$479,210	$413,885		$367,230

From this it is concluded that the reserves of oil are 1,343,000 gross barrels and 1,175,125 net barrels (after royalty).

Anticipated future income, after overhead charges $893,095
Estimated operating costs $479,210
Estimated future profits $413,885
Present worth, discounted at 5% annual rate $367,230

This is equivalent to $367,230/1,175,125 = $0.312 per net barrel in the ground.

At the daily rate of production during January, 1941, of 800 barrels gross, 700 net, the value is equivalent to $525 per net daily barrel.

It is $367,230/$110,900 = 3.3 times the estimated profit of the current year.

Elimination of pennies and odd dollars in the table indicates that it has been prepared by a valuation engineer and not by an accountant.

The effects of income taxes have been omitted in this example because the rates vary in different states and also are controlled by the accounting as to the depreciation and depletion charges against earnings when computing the net taxable income. In general it is wise to assume that income taxes will absorb 25 per cent to 40 per cent of the cash profits which accrue to a corporation owner. When ownership of a property is vested in an individual, the percentage will depend on the surtax brackets which appear in his income tax returns.

Partially developed properties lend themselves less readily to forecasts of future production. The estimates are less positive and require inclusion in the costs column of the amounts required for additional wells and the attendant equipment. The weight of the uncertainties increases with the proportion of the incomplete development because the behavior of the new wells and their productivity and number in any given areal extent can seldom be precisely foretold.

The Influences of Curtailment. The capitalization of income as a means of valuation has many objectionable features, such as price breaks, variations in costs and in demands, and the effects of changes in operating methods and management. The engineering estimate became established as orthodox in oil-field practice when wells were produced to their full capacities and the forecasting of future production rates, as roughly carried out as may have been, had at least more than a touch of mathematical justification. In addition, there was the good general rule that, when anticipatory estimates are carefully based on the records of the past and on the observations of the present, then the band of uncertainties is narrowed.

The widespread adoption of deliberate restriction of well outputs has largely ended the adaptability of decline curves as a guide in estimates of the timing of oil production. The curtailment of wells and the variations in production rates, brought about through changes in the methods of establishing production allotments by the authorities, have increased the difficulties and have made additional information necessary. Fortunately, advances in the means for the volumetric determination of reservoir-oil content, outlined in Chapter IV, have closed a portion of this gap. No formulas, however, point toward a description of the rate at which the oil will be obtained. Probably the current rate should be the standard used in valuations, just as use of the current price of crude appears to be the preferable course. If one is sufficiently daring, he can project an estimated future rate of withdrawal that is based on studies of supply, demand, and as many other intangibles as may suggest recognition, but the conclusions have a limited scope. In each state the conditions differ in regard to permissible production rates; and a few states have no statutory curtailment, whereas others follow various formulas which, in turn, are altered from time to time.

In addition, the efforts to fit production to the changing demand and to the displacement of the principal sources of supply, with more important sources discovered in new localities, all tend to confuse the outlook as to timing.

In consequence, the productive rates from wells are lowered during their early years and are maintained at higher rates during the later period. In other words, the curve has been flattened out somewhat; and with the optimism that characterizes the oil producer he hopes that the final result will include a sufficiently increased ultimate recovery of oil to repay some of the deferment of income he has endured.

Another important effect of the restriction of production has been the increased capital needs for development, caused by the extended time necessary to return the well costs. Ordinarily in the past this item was of no great consequence when wells with a fair flush-production rate would return their costs within four to eight months. With payouts extending to three years and longer, capital requirements for an undeveloped property and the amounts properly chargeable for the use of these funds have become features which may not be ignored in an engineering appraisal of an undrilled property that is situated where the wells are to be severely curtailed.

Pages 146 to 149 illustrate such delayed-production conditions in a valuation of a typical western Texas property which is proved to contain oil by the surrounding developments and is itself as yet undrilled.

Table IV contains the schedule of computations in an engineering type of valuation, based on the assumed facts shown on page 146. The course and details described here are more elaborate than are usually followed. Interest charges may be omitted most of the time as of small consequence, and other variations suggest themselves when different conditions are met. The payout columns are omitted in reports unless a client specifically desires this information. The use of $60 per well-month as a measure of field operating costs may be replaced with $40 per month for the period in which it is believed that the wells will flow; and $90 during the pumping period. It is apparent, also, that any pattern which contemplates a uniform production rate, held throughout a 25-year period, is entirely academic, and warrant for its use is found only in its service as a base from which to consider and visualize the economics and feasibility of a development project.

In this illustration, the outline of the base suggested by the schedule

VALUATION FACTORS

Area	3 labors (531 acres)
Proved well locations	15 (@ 35.4 acres per location)
Oil reserves	4,248,000 barrels (@ 8,000 per acre)
Royalty rate	⅛ (531,000 barrels)
Net oil reserves	3,717,000 barrels (after royalty)
Allowable production rate	960 barrels per well-month
Gas-oil ratio	600 cubic feet
Gravity of oil	31°
Posted market price	$0.94
Overhead costs, for administration, superintendence, office, insurance, land, and gross-production taxes	$0.10
Net income per barrel after overhead	$0.84
Completion cost per well	$28,000
Operating cost per well	$60 per well-month
Interest rate for new money	5%
Discount rate for present worth of future profits after property has cleared the costs of development and operations	6%
Drilling time for completion	36 days
Development requirements	

Year 1   Tankage, storehouse, pumps, etc. $ 15,000
        Drill 10 wells @ $28,000   280,000
        Note. Of this amount, $45,000 is required at the inception of operations and the balance in even amounts throughout the year
        Interest charge

$$5\% \text{ of} \left(\$45,000 + \frac{\$295,000 - \$45,000}{2} \right) \qquad 8,500 \qquad \$303,500$$

Year 2   Drill 5 wells (@ $28,000) $140,000
        Interest charge

$$\$0.05 \times \left(\$271,220 + \frac{\$140,000 - \$106,520}{2} \right) \qquad 14,400 \qquad \$154,400$$

Year 3   No new capital requirement
        Interest charge

$$\$0.05 \times \left(\$319,100 - \frac{\$116,210}{2} \right) \qquad\qquad \$13,030$$

Estimated production

Year 1   No oil during first two months. Thereafter
        10 wells at average of 5 months
                   50 well-months @ 960 barrels   48,000 barrels

Year 2 10 wells @ 12 months   120 well-months
          5 wells @ 9 months   45   do.

          ─────
                          165   do.   @ 960 barrels 158,400 barrels
Year 3 15 wells @ 12 months 180 well-months @ 960 barrels 172,800 barrels

is that the new money requirement for the development of the property will be about $325,000. This amount will be returned from the production profits, plus an interest charge on the unreturned cash advances at a 5 per cent rate of $46,320 at the end of the fifth year, together with $6,110 in the clear. Thereafter an operating profit of $116,210 per year for 20 years, amounting in all to $2,324,200, will accrue from the production of the remaining reserves. The present worth of this future profit, discounted at an annual rate of 6 per cent, is $1,018,600.

Expressed in another way, and this is often a help to the client who is unfamiliar with the meaning of the discounted present worth of future earnings, if $1,018,600 were to be paid for the property and $325,000 in addition were to be made available for the development expenditures, then the latter advance together with interest on it at 5 per cent would be liquidated from the production profits during the first 5 years, and the $1,018,600 would be returned over the ensuing 20 years, together with interest on the unpaid balances at an annual rate of 6 per cent.

The prospective buyer (or seller) can measure and weigh in his own mind, knowing that this identical schedule will never be realized in fact, the relative importance and effects of the various factors. It may be that the production rate will be expedited; the price of oil may change; the operating costs may continue to increase. He may be willing to forego some of the interest charges set up here for the use of development cash advances. He must apply great consideration to the effects of income taxes.

The longer the period covered in an estimate of this kind, the greater is the uncertainty. Departures are much more likely to occur to that part of the schedule which follows the initial 5-year period, during which the property is being developed and the development expenditures and interest are being paid out. The early earnings are the good earnings, both because they are more nearly within the grasp and because they are more certain.

For all practical purposes a satisfactory review of the outlook for this later period may be had by resorting to short cuts. Starting with an assumption that the first 5 years will have cleared the investment in development, it is next desired to learn the present worth of a fixed

TABLE

ENGINEERING

Year	Production		Income at $0.84	Operating Costs	Operating Profit	Interest Charges
	Gross	Net				
	(1)	(2)	(3)	(4)	(5)	(6)
1	48,000	42,000	$ 35,280	$ 3,000	$ 32,280	$ 8,500
2	158,400	138,600	116,420	9,900	106,520	14,400
3	172,800	151,200	127,010	10,800	116,210	13,050
4	172,800	151,200	127,010	10,800	116,210	7,890
5	172,800	151,200	127,010	10,800	116,210	2,408
6	172,800	151,200	127,010	10,800	116,210	
7	172,800	151,200	127,010	10,800	116,210	
8	172,800	151,200	127,010	10,800	116,210	
9	172,800	151,200	127,010	10,800	116,210	
10	172,800	151,200	127,010	10,800	116,210	
11	172,800	151,200	127,010	10,800	116,210	
12	172,800	151,200	127,010	10,800	116,210	
13	172,800	151,200	127,010	10,800	116,210	
14	172,800	151,200	127,010	10,800	116,210	
15	172,800	151,200	127,010	10,800	116,210	
16	172,800	151,200	127,010	10,800	116,210	
17	172,800	151,200	127,010	10,800	116,210	
18	172,800	151,200	127,010	10,800	116,210	
19	172,800	151,200	127,010	10,800	116,210	
20	172,800	151,200	127,010	10,800	116,210	
21	172,800	151,200	127,010	10,800	116,210	
22	172,800	151,200	127,010	10,800	116,210	
23	172,800	151,200	127,010	10,800	116,210	
24	172,800	151,200	127,010	10,800	116,210	
25	172,800	151,200	127,010	10,800	116,210	
	4,180,800	3,658,200	$3,072,930	$261,300	$2,811,630	$46,320

(2) (1) × 0.875.
(3) (2) × $0.84.
(4) Number of well months in operation × $60.
(5) (3) minus (4).

IV

VALUATION

Operating Profit after Interest	Development Costs	Payout at End of Year	Profits after Payout	Present Worth		Year
				Factor	Amount	
(7)	(8)	(9)		(10)	(11)	
$ 23,780	$295,000	−$271,220				1
92,120	140,000	− 319,100				2
103,160		− 215,940				3
108,320		− 107,620				4
113,730		+ 6,110	$ 6,110	0.747	$ 4,560	5
116,210			116,210	0.722	83,900	6
116,210			116,210	0.681	79,140	7
116,210			116,210	0.642	74,610	8
116,210			116,210	0.605	70,310	9
116,210			116,210	0.570	66,240	10
116,210			116,210	0.537	62,400	11
116,210			116,210	0.507	58,920	12
116,210			116,210	0.478	55,550	13
116,210			116,210	0.450	52,290	14
116,210			116,210	0.424	49,270	15
116,210			116,210	0.400	46,480	16
116,210			116,210	0.377	43,810	17
116,210			116,210	0.355	41,250	18
116,210			116,210	0.335	38,930	19
116,210			116,210	0.316	36,720	20
116,210			116,210	0.298	34,630	21
116,210			116,210	0.281	32,660	22
116,210			116,210	0.264	30,680	23
116,210			116,210	0.249	28,940	24
116,210			116,210	0.235	27,310	25
$2,765,310	$435,000		$2,330,310		$1,018,600	

Income taxes, assumed at 17%   173,060

ESTIMATED PRESENT WORTH OF FUTURE PROFITS $ 845,540

(6) (Unreturned capital minus one-half year's profits) × $0.05 (see page 146).
(7) (5) minus (6).
(9) (7) minus (8) plus payout of previous year.
(10) Factor for year 5 taken from Table III, page 134.
    Factors for years 6 and thereafter from Table I, page 130.

profit of $116,210 to be earned each year during a 20-year period. In Fig. 31 it is indicated on the 6 per cent curve that a median point, representative of this period from the sixth to the twenty-fifth year, is about 0.43.

$$\$116,210 \times 20 \times 0.43 = \$999,410$$

It is also possible to ascertain quickly the approximate present worths of different combinations of the timing of future profits. This is illustrated by assuming that the object is to learn the present worth of the total estimated profit of $2,324,200 ($116,210 × 20) which follows the payout, provided a greater portion of this amount is to become available during the early part of the 20-year period. The effect is to conform more nearly to the pattern of the normal slope of a decline curve. Assume that 40 per cent of the total profits will be obtained during the period from year 6 to year 10; 30 per cent more during the following 5 years; and the remaining 30 per cent indefinitely thereafter. The factors which reflect these time periods on the 6 per cent curve in Fig. 31 are about 0.64, 0.42 and 0.24, respectively. The present worth at this assumed recovery rate would be

$$\$2,324,200 \times 0.40 \times 0.64 \qquad \$595,000$$
$$\$2,324,200 \times 0.30 \times 0.42 \qquad \$292,850$$
$$\$2,324,200 \times 0.30 \times 0.24 \qquad \$167,300$$

$$\$1,055,150$$

Notwithstanding that the influence of this change on the estimated worth of the property is slight, it does set up a more inviting picture to the type of buyer who is attracted by a prospect for increased early profits rather than for deferred returns of somewhat greater amounts.

Here again is the significance of the purpose for which a valuation is made and an indication of how the one property may be found simultaneously to have different values for different purposes. This may happen even when the work has been carried out by the same appraiser. An engineering appraisal, computed in accordance with the wish of some one whose desire is the immediate investment of surplus income through the agency of drilling oil wells and whose tax position makes that course especially advantageous, may arrive at a value quite different from what is estimated for a company situated so that it is not prepared to advance development expenses and is, in fact, more concerned with early earnings and dividends in its operating and financial program. The meanings of the expression "value" are very different to these two interests.

Another feature of valuations of the engineering type which has become especially emphasized since curtailment and restrictions of well yields were introduced, and thereby a wider latitude in the supportable estimates of production rates, is the extent to which the figures can be maneuvered in the direction of either high or low results. Experience and dexterity in this artifice can locate an engineering valuation within a considerable range by a judicious combination of timing, interest charges, and discount rates.

PAYOUT METHOD

The *payout* is the practical man's adaptation of the engineering valuation. Long before the engineer adopted the method which carries the stamp of his profession, the buyers of oil properties had become aware of its significance and in the hard way had learned its uses and limitations. Just as in many sales and purchases of income-yielding real estate the transactions are carried out without relying on an extensively computed analysis of the value, so in trades which involve producing oil properties the estimates of their values are often derived from short cuts. They have as their basis, nevertheless, the fundamental idea of a capital account valuation, in an amount such as will be returned with an appropriate rate of either interest or profit, or with both.

Producing oil properties differ from ordinary real estate in that, since the operation has to do with the liquidation of a property in the form of its production and sale in small units, the operators have been less attracted by interest earnings and very much more concerned with an assured and early return of their investment. This reasoning took form in the adoption of payout as a measure of value in terms of the period required to return the cost in cash profits from the operations. It is as firmly established in the oil business as is the unit of front foot for measuring the value of certain forms of real estate, of the subscriber in the value of a newspaper, of the square foot in the value of certain types of buildings. And, as in real estate, its correct use as a yardstick calls for careful and experienced handling. The payout period in transactions of developed oil properties has generally ranged for working interests from four to seven times the annual earnings. Many dealings in royalty interests under wells which are settled and severely curtailed have been transacted for as much as twelve times the annual rate of return.

In trade practice the payout follows two lines, and it is well to clarify this feature in any discussion that contemplates payout as a basis of approach. The time usually referred to means the current annual rate of earning; thus a 4-year payout equals four times the current annual earning rate. However, it can also be taken to mean the sum of the estimated earnings which it is anticipated will be derived during the next 4 years, based on current conditions as to oil and gas prices, costs, and after making allowance for declines in production rates. The question of profits taxes also enters.

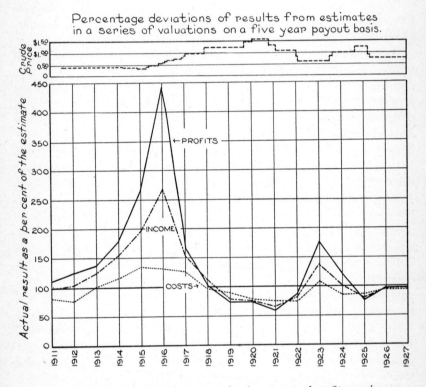

Percentage deviations of results from estimates in a series of valuations on a five year payout basis.

FIG. 34.   Relation of estimated payout valuations to actual profit experiences.

The necessity for careful treatment in the use of this method is illustrated in Fig. 34, a graphic record relating to a producing property in the Midway field. If in 1911 it had been purchased on the basis of a 5-year payout and the then current price of oil and current production costs, with the actual production for the ensuing 5 years definitely known in advance, the outcome would have been very close to the expectation. The reason is that the price of crude remained unchanged during the following 5 years, and the operating costs were

reduced somewhat.   A slight increase in actual profits over the payout estimate resulted.

A similar estimate, made in 1913, would have been found to result
correctly as to the costs, but with the income increased about 25 per
cent over the estimate through the crude-price increase which came
during 1916 and 1917.   The 5-year profits exceeded the estimate by a
substantial amount.   It is important to observe here again the obvious
fact that the inherent inaccuracies of the estimates of oil reserves constitute only one of several elements of uncertainty in a valuation.
Crude prices, costs, and taxes may exert variations far greater in their
percentage effect.

The record of property payouts on a cash basis is a favorite financial
tabulation with oil operators, and one that is very disturbing to accounting experts because it is simple, easily understood, and takes no
account of depletion, depreciation, or interest charges.   It aims at the
difference between the cash income and the cash outgo, and usually
does not contain even such overhead charges as supervision and taxes.
Many companies which have distinguished records of success are found
to have a surprisingly large number of operating properties which are
short of being paid out on this basis.

Since payout as a measure of value is often utilized by sellers and
buyers, it is frequently invoked by appraisers when a valuation is
sought that will be consistent with the market conditions that are
reflected in current transactions.

The device has another important use — as a check on the results
obtained by appraisals which have followed other methods.   When a
valuation figure, ascertained by some other method, is divided by the
approximate current cash-profit rate for the year and the result ranges
from 3 to 12 years, then at least no great inconsistency stands out, provided the property is developed and the oil reserves are fairly well
indicated.   The 3-year side of the range will apply to new properties
where the production rates are flush and are faced with early and
rapid declines.   The long period is applicable to those areas where
ample reserves are proved and the withdrawal rates are so severely
restricted by reason of statutory curtailment that the value of a property is much more a function of its earnings, and its prospects for increases in earnings, than of its estimated oil reserves.   When the
figures fall outside the range indicated, then it is at least a red flag of
warning that possibly a blunder has crept into the valuation.

The payout prospect as to development of undrilled properties is an
important factor in the financing of drilling programs.   This is especially true when the banker enters the picture.   A typical San Joaquin

Valley deep well costs $80,000, produces 3,550 barrels net per month after royalty. The oil, gas, and gasoline products provide a combined revenue equivalent to $1.38 for each barrel of oil produced.

Income per month 3550 barrels @ $1.38		$4899
Total operating costs per month		845
		$4054

$$\frac{\$80,000}{\$4,054} = 19.7 \text{ months' payout}$$

In a Permean Basin locality where the wells cost $30,000 and are permitted to produce 1,080 barrels gross per month, 945 net barrels after royalty, of $0.92 crude, the payout becomes extended.

Income per month 945 barrels @ $0.92		$869
Lifting costs	50.00	
Overhead 945 barrels @ $0.09	85.05	135.05
Operating profit		$733.95
25% provision for income taxes		183.49
		$550.46

$$\frac{\$30,000}{\$550.46} = 54.5 \text{ months' payout}$$

The acceptability of the second outlook as security for a fairly full capital loan may still be satisfactory to a banker; but, when he does consent to a 2-year maturity in the note, he is well aware that when it becomes due an extension will be required for some unpaid and unpredictable balance.

All buyers of properties do not seek an early payout. One group is intent on an inflation hedge, and these buyers much prefer that all or a substantial portion of the earnings be deferred. This point of view increases the attraction of the slow payout, and makes the early earners less attractive. In one unique lease which controls the development of a large property, the lessor has required that only those locations which serve as offset and drainage-protection wells may be drilled.

THE DAILY BARREL

This method expresses the value of a developed, producing property in a rate per daily barrel of oil produced. It preceded the formal presentation of the engineering method as a complete process based

on decline curves and anticipated earnings. It has the merit of simplicity, and it was widely adopted during the early days of the industry,
first in the Appalachian fields and latter carried out to the Mid-Continent areas. The arithmetic was simple. A property, having production considered to be settled, was counted as worth 1,000 times the
price of the crude oil it yielded for each barrel of net daily production
after royalty.

The 1,000 factor was a convenient generalized unit only and served
merely as a starting point for negotiations which might move into
higher ground or drop to lower levels. Crude which sold for $1.00 per
barrel and cost $0.10 to operate returned a profit of $0.90 per barrel
daily, or a profit at the rate of $328.50 per year. With a moderate
rate of decline the outlook suggested a return of the investment in
about 4 years. Taxes and overhead charges were negligible; operating
costs were low; and a feature of much greater weight was the fact that
any declines in productivity rates were balanced by the circumstance
that these transactions usually took place during periods of over-
production and depressed crude prices. A subsequent return of price
schedules to a normal range more than compensated for the well declines.

The method and the measure lack precision and have no direct field
in finished valuation practice. But the unit is a useful one for quick
expressions of relative values and for checking the more elaborate
appraisal computations. An engineering valuation which on completion proves to be such an amount that, when divided by the daily
rate of production, the result is $4,000 per barrel, in a district where
$800 is known to register the general measure of property worth, con-
tains some serious error. It should be reexamined. The appraiser
constantly checks the more complete and well-defined valuations with
this unit test; to do so is not only a safeguard but it also helps him to
gain a background and a cross section of the relative units to be applied
in quick approximations under various circumstances. These units
generally trend toward over-valuations, and this tendency has increased during recent years with the advances in lifting and overhead
costs and with the introduction of income taxes. A haphazard reliance
on the method, without a solid knowledge of the field operating conditions which prevail at the property, is dangerous.

The range of rates is from $400 to $2,500 per net barrel. A producing property which on an analytical appraisal is computed to be worth
an amount equivalent to less than $400 per barrel has probably a
greater worth for its salvable equipment, and the application of this
unit method of value is inappropriate. The range of $500 and $600 per

barrel registers the values of many properties whose wells are mature and are produced to capacity. In this class are the elderly wells which produce high-grade crude of a price in excess of $1.00 per barrel, but with a relatively low yield of 5 to 20 barrels per day, with consequent high operating costs per barrel. Also included are those wells which produce the heavier and less desirable crudes at greater production rates. Wells in the last class which draw from the thick Tertiary sands and which have prospects of longevity increase to $700 to $900 per barrel. The final rate must always be a reflection of the circumstances at the individual property, its situation, the operating conditions, the costs, the crude price, the anticipated life, and the apparent decline rate.

Properties whose production rates are restricted reach substantially higher units, which also depend on many local conditions. Obviously, the well which has been drilled at a cost of $30,000 and produces less than 30 barrels of $0.95 crude per day under curtailment must be worth more than $1,000 per net barrel or else the drilling of the well is an unwise undertaking. Such a well in the Slaughter Pool probably has an expectation of producing ultimately 250,000 barrels net with a total operating cash profit of $175,000, and the owner who has drilled and paid for this well can view the prospect for a profit return of this amount through the future years. For this well he has paid $30,000 in addition to the original cost of the land or lease acquisition. If he has a regard for interest earnings, a view which is not held by a surprisingly large number of oil operators, he will conclude the present worth of these future earnings to be 0.50 of that amount, or $87,500. At a daily rate of 28 barrels this is equivalent to $3,120 per barrel. Few buyers would be willing to purchase at that rate; occasional owners refuse to sell for less because of an emotional pride of ownership, or a tax which the sale might create, or a need for the oil in connection with refinery operations.

Generally, an assortment of Mid-Continent and Gulf Coast and Permean Basin severely curtailed properties will have a combined sales value ranging from $2,000 to $2,500 per net barrel. The prices on the high side reflect unusual degrees of curtailment, advantageous operating conditions, and possibly the complete affair sweetened with some undrilled acreage that holds prospects for coming into the money.

THE WELL

A unique measure of value which is found chiefly in Texas and New Mexico is the well itself. Ordinarily, the production conditions vary too widely, even within short distances, for this type of unit to have significance. Wells which are to be comparably rated must be abundant in number and must have more features in common than usually are found.

The East Texas field conforms to such requirements. It is the most important field in the history of the industry, the most extensive areally; it has about 26,000 producing wells, all shallow and cheaply drilled completions in the one sand and all carefully curtailed to a uniform and consistent pattern. The reservoir is one continuous sand body, the thickness and characteristics of which have been thoroughly documented by the complete coverage of wells.

In this field a completed well, equipped to pump, subject to a one-eighth royalty, has a value that ranges from $13,000 to $60,000. Still lower values are met, but they imply impending exhaustion and a salvage outlook at the end of a short producing period. The average well situated up and down the Fairway is worth about $35,000, with values above and below that median line reflecting chiefly the following factors.

Sand thickness

Presence of water, or proximity to edge-water invasion on the west side of the field

Proximity to either present or past excessive withdrawals of hot oil

Nearness to the east feather edge, and the prospect of being in the way of gas-cap extensions

Density of wells. The number of wells on the property; the number on the offsetting and nearby tracts, and the likelihood of additional wells being drilled on them

The Barrel in the Ground

The value of oil in the ground is a convenient unit of measure at times. To an operating oil company the genuine worth of a barrel in place is at least indicated by the amount which it provides in cash dividends to the stockholder, since the oil business comprises essentially the search for and the production of crude oil. A review has been made of the dividend record of 24 companies (including both integrated companies and those which produce only) over a period of 15 years, during which about 5 billion barrels of oil were produced by these companies. The average disbursement of dividends to common stockholders during that time was equivalent to $0.38 per net barrel of company-interest oil produced. The company which disbursed the lowest rate ($0.072 per barrel) is a large integrated concern, well known for its continued policy of plowing earnings back into the business. In the upper scale (about $0.90 per barrel) are some companies of outstandingly successful records as finders and producers of crude and also the smaller producing units which have long since completed and paid for their development program and are now quasi-liquidating concerns. The equivalent dividend rates during later years, under greater taxes and increased costs for the successful discovery acquisition of new sources of crude, will be found to be markedly lower.

Oil reserves in well-settled properties, fully developed, whose crude brings $1.00 or more per barrel, are fairly worth $0.50 and more per barrel in the Mid-Continent and Gulf Coast areas, and desirable properties on that price basis are not readily obtained. In western Texas and New Mexico values are about $0.35 per net barrel developed; about $0.20 when undeveloped.

Price conditions and values can change rapidly. During 1939 proved properties at Santa Maria were available at prices equivalent to $0.07 to $0.09 per barrel for the reserves in undrilled tracts where excessive withdrawals of hot oil were being taken from adjoining properties. Two years later, under the stimulus provided by a greatly improved demand and posted price together with some measure of order in the field production practices, the values of similar properties had risen to $0.20 and $0.25 per barrel.

Sometimes in the valuation of companies, as differentiated from the valuation of their properties, it is possible to ascertain the records of the amounts which have been spent for exploration and the oil reserves obtained by this means, and to compare this unit of cost with the sums spent for the acquisition of proved properties containing known reserves at the time of purchase. This affords a comparison of the two methods as followed by the company under survey. The investigation is not a simple one and usually meets resistance and much partisan presentation of evidence.

FOR THE LENDER

Restriction of production has brought about marked changes in the financing of oil-field developments. The money lender has come into the situation to an increased extent and performs a very useful service because of the much greater amount of capital outlay required after the discovery of a new field. Prior to 1930 it was a common experience to have the yields from one or two productive wells provide the means with which to pay for the further development account. In fact, it was not an uncommon experience for a discovery or initial well to have flowed sufficient oil to provide the money with which to pay the drilling contractor when he presented his bill. The chief problem was that of finding an immediate purchaser for the crude. Once a pipe line was built to the property, the oil was sold as rapidly as produced. Such exceptions as Cushing and Cleveland, Eldorado, and Midway occurred from time to time, but they were not the rule even though they did flood the market and tend to break prices.

At present the discovery of a new field brings on as a major problem the sale of the oil and the provision of sufficient funds to care for the new drilling because with the very restricted yield now permitted at most new fields the wells seldom return their cost in a period of less than 2 years, and in many areas the time factor is extended to 4 or 5 years. It becomes necessary, therefore, for the operator to meet extensive outlays, and this he may do either from his own funds, or from the sale of an interest in his property (thereby diluting his portion) or by borrowing. Borrowing is a simple and direct course.

The examination of a property as security for a loan is more simple than when a purchase is being considered. The sole objective is to measure it as a safeguard for the loan, and relatively little consideration need be given to those elements which may have great importance in a buy-and-sell test but have little effect on the earnings with which the interest and instalment payments are to be met. Some features take on added importance because lenders normally do not wish to enforce foreclosures. Banks do not desire to take over oil properties and go into the oil business; they want only to feel assured that the loan will be paid and, if not, that the property will find a ready buyer at a price adequate to take them out. Therefore, such speculative phases as deep-sand prospects, possible increases in the price of oil, improved field operation, and comparable topics which are highly material in the usual valuation are entirely secondary in a report prepared for a lender who requires only to know the indicated capacity of the property to earn the interest and the sinking-fund requirements.

In addition to the banks and the private lending agencies which make loans of this kind, the pipe-line crude-oil purchasing companies also advance funds to the producer in order to have a preferred position for the purchase of the crude. Such advances usually work out satisfactorily, but when they do not the lender then finds that he has bought the property instead of just having loaned money on it. This latter contingency is obviously the reason for employing the appraiser, and its avoidance should be the principal guide in the examination.

Often the proposed terms of a loan may not conform to what is expected from the production and earnings, notwithstanding that the property has much value. The payments should bear some relation to the declining rates of production, especially in flush fields. To illustrate, a loan application is for $450,000, payable at $25,000 per month over an 18-month period. Cash earnings are currently at $55,000 per month, but an examination discloses a rapid decline rate in the production and points to a probable rate during the latter part of the 18 months that is dangerously close to the scheduled payment requirements. Then, if a reduction in crude price should occur, the borrower may find himself unable to meet the payments. It is often feasible to rewrite a payment schedule so that it conforms to the pattern of expected profits and thereby is converted to an acceptable form. In the foregoing example, monthly payments during each of the 6-month periods of $35,000, $25,000, and $15,000 provide a pattern more nearly reflecting the production outlook.

A type of bank loan which has been widely exploited during recent years has taken the form of a three-way arrangement between the producer, the contract well driller, and the bank. This arises where much drilling is to be carried out at a property which is fully proved, but where the permitted rate of production is so small that several years will be required to return the cost of the well completions. The drilling contractor undertakes to drill and complete the wells at an agreed price and to take payment in the form of a percentage of the sales of oil from the wells until the account is cleared, plus interest on the unpaid balances. The bank advances to the contractor the necessary funds, and everyone makes money because this type of loan is founded on ample evidence that the wells have reserves from which to pay the accounts. Dry holes are paid for in full on completion. The appraiser's function is to check the estimates of the reserves, the outlook for oil sales, and to make sure that the project is technically sound.

At the time that a loan is being considered the extent of the clearly proved area may not be outlined. The problem is then less simple and the appraiser does little more than to define the situation as to the established locations for wells and for those which appear promising, and to express his judgement in a less formal manner than in an elaborate valuation report. It usually follows that the lender proceeds more deliberately and advances sums from time to time as the information disclosed in the progress of the work warrants.

Unwillingness of banks in the past to take long positions with respect to oil property loans and, in fact, the genuine fear and aversion of bankers toward oil loans have been a great blessing to the oil fraternity. This attitude has often retarded the more venturesome members from becoming too extended and probably accounts more than any other reason for the fact that, during periods of depression in the industry, few producers fail and few properties are to be had at forced sale prices. The operators were not permitted to borrow to such an extent that they were carried under when crude prices were reduced. They were saved because the bankers had been unwilling to make loans which really involved no greater risks than banks undertake regularly in other business enterprises with which they are more familiar.

A valuation for the use of lenders, accordingly, need seldom be as complete and thorough an examination of every feature of the property value when they do not relate to the prospects for cash operating profits which are to be available toward the payment of a proposed loan. It is a duty of the examiner to disclose to his client whatever information is pertinent as to the character and ability of the borrower, and especially to spell out the nature and scope of the risks in a loan, with respect both to the repayment schedule and to the sale value of the property in the event of a loan failure.

It is not the province of the appraiser to judge finally the merit of a loan application even though an examination often leads some distance beyond the mere testing of oil reserves and anticipated profits. The borrower's plans may contemplate the drilling of new wells, or the purchase of an old property, or the concentration into one account of many scattered obligations to supply houses.

A loan secured by a single well is never good banking practice. Assured sale of the crude production is necessary. The salvable equipment at an operating property is undesirable collateral. It is sound reasoning to be more sympathetic toward a loan application from a capable operator who purposes using the money to purchase and rehabilitate a poorly operated property than toward a loan for the purpose of drilling additional town-lot wells which are not necessary for the efficient recovery of the underground oil.

Loans that are based on an assumption that production rates are to be continued in excess of the statutory or umpire allowables are vulnerable. It is wise to verify statements of production from either the pipe-line ledger of the seller or the monthly statements supplied him by the buyer. This is less easily done when the oil is conveyed by truck to some independent refiner. Comparison can be made with the official oil allowables. Unusual earnings may have been the result not of oil produced but from the sale of surplus equipment, a source that is obviously nonrecurring.

When those loan proposals that are manifestly inappropriate have been eliminated, the lending of money, based on oil-producing properties as security, is a splendid banking operation. The larger forms of this type of business are the bond issues of considerable size. The record of these issues is unique in the negligible portion that have turned sour. The reason for this is simple. The producing oil properties which secure most large bond issues have an extraordinary capacity for liquidation as compared with the properties back of utility and other industrial issues. In almost any circumstance of unusual demand or need for funds, the oil company has only to stop spending new money and let the wells pump their way out. For that reason few bonds of producing oil companies have failed, except where there have been obvious fraud and dishonesty.

THE ROYALTY

The term has its origin in the old common law of England. Land titles were vested in the crown, and the occupants or tenants worked the land, grew the crops, and rendered a share of the crops to the royal owner of the land. The working interest did the work and paid the bills. The royalty was a portion of the product which under the royal decree passed to the landowner. A royalty, therefore, has been defined as " a share of the production or profits reserved by the owner for permitting another to use or develop his property " (*Texas Sulphur Company* vs. *Guaranty B. & T. Co.*, 4, Fed. 2d, 662).

Accordingly, an oil royalty, at least in theory, is an interest in the oil and gas produced from a property without any charge levied against it for the costs for either development or operations. As items of property, royalty interests are widely dealt in; they take the diverse forms described in Chapter II, and these forms affect their value. The estimates required in the course of an appraisal are less elaborate than those concerned with a lessee interest because costs demand little consideration.

Oil Reserves. The estimates of reserves should be as carefully compiled as in the examination of a working interest. The timing of the oil recoveries is usually of greater interest and consequence to the landowner whose only oil income is from the one property. Generally, the landowner prizes the prospect of early earnings and has no wish for a greater return that is spread over a deferred period. A smaller number prefer some deferment, and some indication of the status of this prospect is in order in a valuation report because, if the oil is to be produced quickly, this may prove to be either desirable or objectionable in the mind of a possible buyer.

The fact that the lessee is the producing department of an integrated company may be advantageous or it may be disadvantageous. Frequently the ownership of refining and marketing units makes a backlog of oil reserves essential, and this can promote a program of development and production which seriously retards the income, suits the lessee interest best, and fails to conform to the anticipations of the lessor.

Payments for Oil, Gas, and Natural Gasoline. The royalty portion of the oil sold to the pipe-line buyer is usually paid directly by the buyer to the lessor under the terms of the division order. The small fractional royalty interests, of which there may be a great many tiny portions, each held by a different person, are not sent the records of detailed accounting; a disbursing agent or trustee receives and holds the monthly royalty payment and settlement record of oil sold, and allocates this among the many small owners.

Appraisals which precede the actual development of production, at properties which are known to contain oil, require that the returns for products must be estimated. If the property is in operation, the average return per barrel for the oil and for the revenue received from sales of gas and gasoline is obtained from the monthly settlement sheets put out by the buyer.

Costs. Notwithstanding the initial simplicity of the lessor position, in regards not bearing any of the expenses or operating charges, many leases do provide that the lessor accept minor expense items, and nearly all lease forms in some way provide a charge for the lessor portion of the natural gasoline obtained from the casinghead gas.

The treatment of emulsified crude for converting it to acceptable pipe-line oil is commonly included as a charge against the royalty oil for its share. The cost per barrel of clean oil turned out is from $0.01 to $0.04, and usually around $0.02.

Disbursement agents or trustees, when called on to act as recipients of the royalty and to apportion it among a number of owners of fractional portions, charge from $0.25 to $1.50 per check issued, in addition to some fixed service fee.

Another class of charges against so-called royalty interests is found in the *participating royalty*. This form usually originates in a contribution toward the cost of drilling a well, and a further fixed monthly contribution toward the maintenance expenses. In return, the owner of the interest receives a portion of the oil or of the receipts from its sale. Unlike the landowner royalty, it expires with the lease. Another limitation is the narrowing of the spread between income and the expense charge when the production rate reaches a low level. The operating contribution is a constant, whereas the income is a variable and usually a decreasing element; the profit margin, therefore, diminishes more rapidly than does the production.

Taxes. This topic is reviewed in Chapter V. Leases provide that the lessor interest pay its ratable portion both of the mineral land taxes and of the severance or gross-production taxes. In addition to these taxes, the state and federal income taxes are to be considered, and they must take into account the specific situation and purpose of the valuation. The tax position of an owner and his status with respect to depletion charges against income in the computation of taxable income are of primary importance in any valuation made for a person who is concerned with the net return of future earnings after taxes.

Unusual Lease Terms. Most leases follow conventional lines, but sometimes they contain unusual stipulations or conditions, such as expiration dates, minimum or advance royalty payments, lessor's contributions or liabilities. The assignment of fractional interests, where the landowner has disposed of a part of his royalty, may reserve to him the right to amend certain terms and features. In a valuation they call for some definite description and outline of their influence.

The Lessee. A capable and energetic producer who drives actively for the early and maximum production strengthens the value of a royalty. A lessee who lags and is less aggressive or who is without funds with which to maintain a competitive position as to offsets, thus permitting the property to suffer drainage, is a detriment to the value. It is undesirable to have the working interest held by an independent refiner who runs the oil to his own plant and accounts for it with statements of doubtful authenticity, difficult to check and still more difficult to disprove.

Ownership by the lessee of the production rights to an adjoining tract on which the royalty rate is lower is a disturbing feature. Similarly, ownership by the lessee or his employees of royalty interests under contiguous tracts promotes distrust and suspicion.

Markets for Royalties. An objection to royalty interests as investments is that no central exchange or market exists where a ready sale can be arranged. Examination for an intending purchaser should take account of the expenses to be incurred in the transfer and assignment of the purchase. Blue-sky regulations and the accompanying legal expenses in certain states prove to be a considerable burden.

During recent years many of the largest transactions in royalty interests have grown out of buyers' quests for hedges against the adverse effects of inflation. This type of buyer is not concerned with early payout and early earnings, but is much occupied with the estimate of recoverable oil in the ground.

Fair Market Value

Engineers invade many situations and they are often repulsed. One field in which this has happened is that of fair market value, for this is a legal term and is an estimate which must conform to the requirements of the law and not to the rational processes of the more usual engineering and analytical appraisal methods. Accordingly, without pretense at interpreting the law and the frequent and often-conflicting court decisions relating to it, the appraiser should inform himself of the legal phases and requirements in each undertaking where market value is to be the guide. Generally, it can be assumed that " market value " and " fair market value " are synonymous terms.

Fair market value is exclusively a legal term; its origin is in the law and there is its field. It is a synthetic expression and traditionally has come to mean that amount which would be paid at a specific time by a buyer, able and willing to buy, and accepted by a seller, willing but not forced to sell, with both buyer and seller having a reasonable knowledge of the facts. The basis is, therefore, an assumption of a hypothetical trade or deal between an imaginary seller and an imaginary buyer. Unhappily the courts in their usual endeavor to fit a single yardstick to many widely different conditions have failed to keep up with progress in the art of valuation by improving the legal technique or by clarifying the inconsistencies of decisions. Conflicts of decisions in various jurisdictions are completely bewildering, and for this reason a valuation relating to fair market value must be predicated as to its nature and limitations upon a full definition from legal counsel.

In other words, whereas the appraiser is generally permitted a great latitude of choice in the course to be followed in a valuation, here he must be guided and controlled by the law and by its interpreter — the lawyer. The appraiser must be patient and sympathetic. He must remember that, even if the hypothetical conception of the willing buyer and the willing seller is a fiction, it is one that has become established by legal usage and must be followed. The law seems to be fond of hypothetical situations and people; possibly they are more tractable and responsive than their real counterparts, especially among the engineers. The shock we receive when we come to learn that we cannot reform our parents is slight compared with the shock to the engineer who attempts to reform court procedure.

When the engineer has examined a property and has ascertained the available facts regarding it, he finds great difficulty in denying himself a forecast or an estimate of the profits and earnings. This comprises in its orthodox form the estimates of future recoverable oil, the future cash income, costs, profits, etc. He then may gild this lily with a discount factor which both articulates future earnings into present value and throws an aura of precision over the reckoning. But the lawyer then warns him that this compilation is an engineering or analytical appraisal and that an estimate of fair market value, derived from this source, is not esteemed favorably by the courts or by the administrative authorities. The engineer may know to his own satisfaction that, in general, the trading range of a property is between 60 and 65 per cent of the analytical appraisal which has followed a 5 or 6 per cent annual discount rate, applied to the estimated future profits; but this kind of solution to the problem is not acceptable.

Unfortunately no single rule can be set up as an acceptable specific guide. The essential feature is the fundamentally established assumption of the willing seller and the willing buyer. These hypothetical traders should be considered familiar with all the necessary facts, fair and reasonable in their views, but nevertheless bent on acting in their own behalf and to their own best advantage, and yet feeling the spirit of compromise to such a degree that their ideas become adjusted and their minds meet on that sanctified spot which the law says is fair market value.

They are truly remarkable persons. Obviously, such a concept does not include buyers and sellers who are broke, or who have that pride of ownership which usually accompanies the successful completion of a wildcat well, or landowners who are unreasoning and simply defy the land leaser who seeks some basis on which to deal. Nor can it be the landowner who is willing to lease but who struggles for a higher price than his neighbors have received merely because of a habit or pride in holding out in such situations. The type is well known and the leasers have a way of dealing that frequently leads to paying an increased price in order to close a block. Such transactions do not reflect a general price value or level because they are closed under some sort of duress and on the theory that the increment can be diluted over the entire block of land that has been acquired.

Generally, fair market value implies conditions of relative stability. Possibly, " normal " conditions would be a fitting term, except that in the oil business normal times are never encountered. Certainly, such extremes as appeared during the 1920 boom when Kansas crude rose to $3.50, or during the 1931 slump at East Texas which found crude selling for 10 cents, are not representative yardsticks for a fair measure of property values. If for no other reason than that almost no properties at the times cited did sell at levels which reflected those temporary crude prices, they are not representative.

Market price should not be confused with fair market value. The former designates those prices at which properties actually do sell even though, and possibly because, the buyers are not thoroughly informed. Or there may be other reasons. Thus the fact that several hundred purchasers have been found who did buy certain undesirable subdivision lots at exorbitant prices has been rejected in courts as evidence of fair market value. Presumably, similar reasoning would apply to the prices received for fractional oil royalty interests which have been distributed at fantastically high prices. It is true that a property may be especially adapted to an owner's use, and thereby be worth more to the owner or to a purchaser than the market value. This appears to be the general trend of thought in a multiplicity of rather conflicting court decisions; but they are found invariably to contain some tangible, unique feature of utility which justifies in a commercial sense the increment of value.

It is apparent, therefore, that the estimate of fair market value must rely upon a series of conceptions, all of which are hypothetical, as to what these fictional characters — the willing seller and the willing buyer — would do at a given time and place. Valuation, considered as a problem in estimation, becomes an art which may encounter its greatest difficulties in this field. It is predicated upon the assumption of a transaction which did not occur, and it requires judgement, skill, experience, speculation, and a considerable measure of imagination.

The law says that the estimating of value is a process that derives from certain classes of evidence, and then the law follows that statement with widely diverse court rulings on the use and admissibility of various types of evidence. Those types of evidence which are generally not allowable in court proceedings, and which therefore are unsafe to use as a foundation for the derivation of a valuation, are original cost, reproduction cost, replacement less depreciation. In one form or another they are all quite conventional in connection with public utility rate cases and with other court and commission proceedings, but ordinarily they will not prove acceptable for establishing fair market value. Even if they were, the values of oil properties are too mercurial to remain related to cost for long, and they are too seldom found identical in qualities to permit measurement by a yardstick of replacement. Reproduction as a measure is out of the question at any time.

Earnings, as indicative of fair market value, generally have been unacceptable to the courts; but the rule on earnings is not so inflexible as on cost and replacement. Current earnings, past earnings, and the prospect for their continuance can often be brought in, even though it is necessary to drag them in by the hair.

That which the courts require and respond to best is the kind of evidence that is based upon a study of actual sales. If no such data may be had, then the appraiser is forced to turn to other sources, but only as a last resort.

Procedure. Oil properties are too unlike to permit direct comparisons of nearly identical units. In order to have a groundwork upon which to build any conclusions, it is well to acquire as much information as can be obtained. This information falls into two classes: (1) the records of actual sales and (2) the comparison of those properties which have sold with the property being studied.

Records of Actual Sales. County records are a primary source of these data; the title and abstract companies compile and supply such information. If it is to be used in court, the legal guidance should dictate the form in which it is assembled because county clerks are seldom willing to certify such compilations. The abstract report should contain the following information for each transaction.

Instrument, whether deed, lease, mineral interest, etc.

Grantor, the name, and address if it has been recorded

Grantee or lessee, with address

Date, both the date of execution of the instrument and the date of recording

Description, legal description of the land

Consideration, including the revenue stamps shown. If photostats are ordered, a separate instruction for the revenue stamps account is necessary because the law requires that photographs of stamps must be obliterated

The records seldom reveal the actual considerations for which properties have sold. The federal stamp tax of 50 cents for each $500 of consideration in the transfer will often provide a fairly close indication, but this evidence is difficult to introduce in court. The names and addresses may be genuine or they may be fictitious; if the people are real, they will often respond to an inquiry about prices — but not always truthfully. The land departments of oil companies keep records of the offerings made to them, and even though such offerings do not constitute transactions they do supply a background of pertinent information regarding the activities of sales efforts and the price ranges during specific periods. Brokers who deal in leases and other properties know what is going on and what the prevailing prices are, but they are more prone to recall the past in generalities. Thus it is necessary to get them away from the broad sweeping statements and to pin them down to specific and concrete descriptions of actual transactions either in which they took part or about whose facts they genuinely know.

Not infrequently the records are found to be misleading about dates, and the actual transactions may prove to have been made long before the papers were filed with the county recorder. In this respect a check of the date on the instrument or the date of the notarial acknowledgement will sometimes untangle seeming discrepancies.

Other sources of information are the newspapers and trade journals and the company scout reports. The trade journals delineate the business conditions which have prevailed during any specific period, particularly the prices of crude oil, the relation of production to consumption and to the accumulation of stocks or the drawing out of stocks, the activities in the buying of properties. These sources also indicate additional avenues of inquiry and the scenes of the greatest interest in new areas at any given time.

Unproved Lands. The great majority of transactions in the oil fields involve nonproducing, unproved leaseholds. Sales of proved and productive properties are relatively few in number.

Unproved, prospective leases have rapidly shifting values which do not lend themselves to formulas. The dates of transactions and the prices paid are intimately related to the oil developments, and these factors are assembled in a chronological account when an estimate of fair market value is sought.

First come the early exploratory activities of the geologists, the geophysicists, and even the ubiquitous doodlebug-machine operator; then the block leasing by the initial operator and the ensuing competitive buying from other sources; the actual drilling of a prospect well; the inevitable account, during the drilling of every wildcat well, that the formations are running high; and finally the successful completion of a producer which heralds the opening of a new field or the abandonment as a failure. Even the usually persistent report, after the abandonment of a dry hole, that " oil was found but they plugged the hole and moved away " affects land prices if not values. And, if some one observes the drilling crew burning their old overalls (in order to conceal evidence of the oil they have struck) an added force is given to the home-town dislike of all oil men who fail to find oil for the chamber of commerce, and the tendency of land prices to hold up continues for a considerable period.

Proved Lands. Thus with nonproducing acreage the prices and values shift rapidly, responsive to the stages in the cycle of a prospective oil field. The acre has been the unit of value for trading purposes. After the field has been discovered and has taken form as a proved area, the acre gives way to the lump sum. The area of a tract is always of consequence, but the chief thought becomes directed to the well locations, oil reserves and operating conditions, and the prospects for profits from the crude production.

Comparison of Properties. It is rarely possible to make simple and direct comparisons. Not only are the time factors seldom identical, but the important agencies of size, shape, and geographic and geologic situations differ. The terms in leases differ as to periods, development requirements, rentals and royalty rates, offsets and other provisions. All must be taken into account and weighted.

The foregoing is true for all classes of properties, both proved and unproved. Comparisons increase in complexity when the properties have moved into the proved and producing class. In the same oil field, where the type of oil occurrence is uniform, wells may differ widely in many respects which affect their productivity and profit yield. The relative importance ascribed to the various influences and the adoption of dissimilar yardsticks can provide a semblance of authenticity to extremely different answers. Recognition of this fact and adroit manipulation of figures can be made to yield surprising results.

No single course is applicable to all situations in this problem. If actual transactions of closely comparable properties have taken place within an appropriate time, an estimate is readily reached. However, irregularities usually are abundant and interfere with any simple, consistent comparison of two properties. The estimator then does well to observe from as many points of view as he can adopt and still rely on for reasonable consistency. The important considerations comprise the estimates of oil reserves, the crude-price structure, the costs, development factors, physical condition of the wells, offsets on competitive properties, and salability of the oil. All these considerations affect an estimate of future profits and, accordingly, are reflected in the relative values of properties. The capital requirements for the new money necessary for development and the timing of the expected profits introduce the question of money market conditions.

Title questions, presumably, are beyond the province of the appraiser, but occasionally they are met and cannot be ignored. Nothing appears to bring out the weaknesses in land titles as does the discovery of oil in a neighborhood.

The assembly of these different items of fact and conclusions is attended with some confusion. A careful weighing of all the data usually simplifies the problem and points the way to a reasonable and convincing solution. All the discrepancies will not be reconciled; but even a review of the probable mental steps that are followed by typical buyers and sellers, and of the outward form taken in such steps, will help clarify the conception of the basis upon which their minds would finally meet. To a realist it is all very absurd; but it is the law, and it can be made intriguing and interesting if one brings himself and his reasoning processes playfully to array the buyer and the seller in a series of imaginative negotiations.

Fair Market Value of Securities. At times the stock of a corporation instead of specific real property is to be valued. Then is introduced another variable into the problem because the prices and the trading values of stocks seldom coincide with the fair market value of the underlying assets. As to stocks which are actively traded in, the quotations and records of sales supply a guide for the courts and the administrative bodies. Many securities, however, are inactive; and, without a record of sales, it is in order to assume that the regard in which they would be held by the investing public would be influenced by additional considerations, such as the character of management, the corporation policies as to dividends and expansion activities, the past record of accomplishments, and the effects on earnings of corporation taxes.

Informative comparisons often may be obtained by placing the company which is being studied beside similar companies whose securities are active, and which thereby supply an indication of how they are regarded by buyers and sellers.

Court Appearances. *Fair market* value being primarily a legal matter, valuations of that type appear in the courts more often than other forms. They bring with them the appraisers, generally much subdued by the curious legal restraint. In some districts the engineer's presentation is permitted considerable freedom; but the general rule is that the appraiser first describes his qualifications as an expert, then describes the property, states his sources of information regarding it, and concludes with a statement of his estimate of the fair market value in one single sum. The admissibility of various types of evidence differs somewhat from state to state, and so do the rules of court procedure; but usually he may not embellish his simple statement with any supporting accounts of how the conclusion was reached, of the several elements which may have been combined in order to build up the final figure, or of the details of actual transactions and how these were interpreted and applied.

When asked the basis of his valuation, the engineer states that it is his estimate of the consideration for which the property would have sold on the specific date in a transaction between a buyer willing and able to buy and a seller who was willing but not forced to sell, with both of them having knowledge of the facts. In other words, he concludes his testimony with no details whatever beyond the one cold figure — this without the benefit of support for his opinion — and with no play of histrionics. It is obviously an advantage to the witness to be endowed with the it's-so-because-I-say-so quality which impresses all juries and occasionally impresses a judge.

Under an ensuing cross examination it is the privilege of the opposing counsel to interrogate the witness on those features which have been barred in the direct testimony. He may be called on for the facts which he found, for his interpretation of them, and for an explanation of the steps of reasoning through which he reached his conclusion. He may have to defend them, although rarely is he put to the test. Lawyers can gauge when such questions are likely to set the stage for the witness to put point and force into his original testimony.

Thus, fair market value is unique and is still undefined. The comment of Randolph E. Paul, in his *Studies in Federal Taxation,* is a sufficient summary.

> It is a weary task to find fair market value. The result is not academic; it expresses itself in money deficiencies. . . . Valuation is neither crystal gazing, nor geometry, but a serious hard business with economic and social implications of vast significance. . . . One must look in many directions at the same time, invoke a host of details, and yet avoid a microscopic attitude.

REFERENCES

Alvey and Foster, *Barrel Day Values,* American Institute of Mining Engineers, Volume 65, 1921.

Ralph Arnold, *Problems of Oil Lease Valuation,* American Institute of Petroleum Engineers, 1919.

R. W. Brown, *Valuation of Oil and Gas Lands,* 1924.

William Forstner, *The Valuation of Oil Lands,* Mining and Scientific Press, Volume 103, p. 578, 1911.

T. A. Hall, "Appraisal of Oil Properties," *Drilling and Production Practice,* American Petroleum Institute, 1939.

H. C. Humphreys, "Payout Status of Oil and Gas Producing Properties," *Oil Weekly,* Dec. 24, 1926.

M. E. Lombardi, *The Valuation of Oil Lands and Properties,* International Engineering Congress, Paper 152, San Francisco, 1915.

Earl Oliver, "Appraisal of Oil Properties," *Mining and Metallurgy,* February, 1920

L. S. PANYITY, " Valuation of Properties in the Bradford District," *Petroleum Development and Technology,* American Institute of Mining Engineers, 1926.

RANDOLPH E. PAUL, *Studies in Federal Taxation,* 1937.

E. W. SHAW, *The Principles of Natural Gas Land Valuation,* American Association of Petroleum Geologists, 1919.

CHAPTER VII

THE EXAMINATION AND REPORT

The way of an appraiser is not easy, even when luck is with him. An important responsibility, no matter what the purpose or object of a valuation, is to compile and record all the available facts. From them he draws his conclusions about types of oil reserves and the extent and nature of their occurrence, the quality and worth of the oil and gas, and the costs of their recovery. A second and equally important responsibility is that of presenting these facts and conclusions clearly so that a careful reader is left with no doubt as to which are the known facts, which are the reasonably adopted assumptions, which are the guesses, and finally which is the part played by each of these classes in the conclusions.

THE DATA

In the confusion and disorder that is usual at the beginning of an investigation of any size, the appraiser's course seems to fit the definition of an expert as " one who brushes aside the minor errors in order to press on to the grand fallacy."

Some perspective is necessary as early as possible, and it is well to gather the available data and to have them arranged and correlated before any field inspection begins. Out of this compilation emerges some measure of the scope and nature of the undertaking, the inquiries to be made, and the relative weights of the items which make up the project. The initial move is an authentic list and description of the properties.

For unproved, prospective acreage the essential data are simple, except in occasional legal and controversial matters, and they are outlined in Chapter II and in the Fair Market Value account of Chapter VI. For producing properties the data will vary with the nature of the appraisal, but most of the required information is to be found in the records of the operator.

Logs of the wells and a map of the property and of the nearby developments are essential. They supply an historical picture and an outline of the status of development of the property and of the contiguous tracts. The record of past production, preferably by individual wells, is obtained and is checked against the pipe-line ledger of oil runs. The production records occur in several forms. The daily pumper's report from the morning gauge states the fluid produced, but not necessarily the amount of clean marketable oil. The monthly report of production is a more exact indication of the amount of clean oil. The monthly record of net pipe-line runs or of oil sold and delivered is the final record. Over a period of several months the record of oil produced and the oil delivered should tally, but in any single month the oil sales are either under or over the actual amount of oil produced.

The books supply specific information regarding costs of overhead and of operations. An inspection of the operating financial record or of the profit-and-loss statement indicates the items of greatest weight. The financial record and list of properties may suggest that some property units are as yet not fully paid for. The appraiser should keep in mind an effort to conform his requirements and the manner of their compilation to the form in which these can be most readily taken from the records. He should avoid calling for new arrangements of data, or asking for special and elaborate statements, because generally the information needed by him is available in some workable form, even though he may never find that form to be identical in any two sets of books.

When the statistical data have been assembled and a fairly clear outline thereby provided of the project and of the further information required, the next source is in the field. Here, also, the conditions may be studied and the operations observed while collection of the additional data is carried out.

The Examination

One of the compensations for the confusion and inconveniences experienced in valuation work is the opportunity to observe many types of field and office operations. One learns early that there is no single formula for success in the business of finding and producing oil; that success has come to men of extreme contrasts in learning, energy, character, thoroughness. Mr. Hendrik Colijn, the Dutch premier, says " Each bird sings a song according to its own throat "; and this is certainly true for oil men also.

In the majority of valuations an inspection of the property is an essential part of the work, and even when this is not considered to be obligatory the appraiser will invariably be rewarded for spending as much time in the field as is consistent with the scope and nature of the job. The general condition of the equipment and its sufficiency can be noted — the needs for repairs on the surface and in the wells — and additional suggestions and ideas always result from the gossip and conversation which accompany a field trip.

Notwithstanding that considerations of character and ability in the management of a property concern a study of the company rather than of the property, past managements may have injured properties through harmful withdrawal rates or through other damaging practices. Statistical records may have been distorted. An examination on the ground will often disclose that some of the statements or representations have been misleading, or other and vital information may be ascertained. The amount of tankage may not conform to the reported production rate; the dehydration equipment may be larger than that required for the amount of water reported to be accompanying the oil; or large volumes of water may be observed draining from gunbarrel tanks at supposedly clean wells. Pipe fittings may be lighter than necessary to care for the pressures reported existing in the wells; derricks may need repairs; obsolete machinery may require replacement; or the equipment may not be well balanced for economical operations.

Deliberate and well-considered deception is almost impossible to detect, short of very elaborate investigations, and such situations rarely arise. Uncle Murray Doan, the David Harum of the oil business, loved to expound that most oil men are honest enough for all practical purposes. On the other hand, some tiny exaggerations creep into the discussions of a transaction and into the descriptions of a property; and memories fail to disclose some obviously detrimental features which probably would never have become known to the appraiser in a valuation which failed to go beyond an " office " examination. These features are rather likely to come to light during a field visit.

ACCOUNTING

The valuation engineer in his dual role as engineer and economist is often confronted with various phases of accounting problems; and, whether or not he enjoys them, it has become an increasingly necessary requirement that he be sufficiently familiar with accounting practices to review and to discuss interpretations of a balance sheet, a profit-and-loss statement, and the ordinary supplemental statistical records which he may encounter and need. To that end he will find it helpful to study the annual reports of oil companies and to note the manner of presenting information to stockholders.

In addition to the annual reports to stockholders, most companies prepare monthly operating financial statements which show the statistical accounts of the sources of income and of the avenues of expense. Accounting methods are far from uniform, and quite different ideas are held about keeping records. The appraiser will meet these disparities in many forms in the various offices; and, as already noted, he should undertake to utilize the data in the form in which they are available rather than to adopt a course which approaches a reconstruction of the books merely in order that his own convenience and ideas about the assembly of these facts may be observed. It usually happens that with some patience and a discussion of the meaning and significance of the accounting headings used, the information can be had without unnecessary confusion and in such shape that misunderstandings of the scope of the figures are avoided. Invariably " lifting costs " and " overhead costs " will be found to contain different classes of items in the books of different companies. It is the appraiser's duty to accept and use this information as he encounters it and not to remake the books.

The basic purpose and duty of any system of accounting is to show (1) the things owned (the assets) and the debts and obligations to stockholders (the liabilities), the two appearing together as a balance sheet; and (2) the profits or the losses, being the difference between the income and the expense which has resulted from the conduct of affairs over a stated period (the profit-and-loss statement).

The Balance Sheet. The balance sheet, as an expression of the assets and liabilities, divides them according to the degree of liquidity or ready convertibility into cash. The current assets include cash, notes receivable, accounts receivable and currently due for goods and services, and inventories. Current liabilities are the obligations due in the normal transactions of the business, such as accounts payable and notes payable.

The fixed assets and fixed liabilities are the frozen items such as the capital, properties, equipment, and the facilities for conducting the business; also such long-term obligations as notes.

Working capital is the excess of current assets over current liabilities. The financial records of large companies which possess widespread interests and obligations in many forms are usually found to be complex and involved. Their interpretation requires the guidance of an experienced accountant.

The essential features of a simple balance sheet are comprised in the illustrative form below.

ANDOR OIL COMPANY

Balance Sheet

December 31, 1941

Assets			Liabilities	
Current Assets			*Current Liabilities*	
Cash on hand		$120,180	Accounts payable	$ 7,210
U. S. Government securities at cost		86,570	Accrued liabilities for payrolls, taxes,	
Current accounts receivable		26,480	etc.	14,240
Notes receivable		20,000	Short-term notes	180,000
Inventories				
Crude oil in storage	$8,360			$201,450
Warehouse materials and supplies	11,970	20,330		
		$273,560	*Funded Debt*	400,000
Fixed Assets			*Capital Stock*	
Lands and leases	$242,000		4,000 shares at $100	400,000
Oil wells	836,000			
	$1,078,000		Surplus	198,110
Less depreciation and depletion	152,000	926,000		
		$1,199,560		$1,199,560

The story indicated by this balance sheet is that the things owned and the amounts due stand at $1,199,560. The current obligations and the funded debt amount to $601,450. The difference between these two, $598,110, is the *indicated net worth* of the company, equivalent to $149.53 per share for the 4,000 shares which represent ownership of the company.

The statement of fixed assets is not conclusive as an expression of the value of the properties. It is merely a showing of the cost of the properties as entered originally on the books. The amortization, that is the amounts subsequently written off for depreciation and depletion of capital assets, is usually shown as a step in the procedure of reaching the net amount at which the fixed assets are carried.

Assume that a valuation of the lands, leases, oil wells, and other properties establishes their worth at $1,100,000. The net worth computation then becomes

Current assets	$ 273,560
Fixed assets (as appraised)	1,100,000
	$1,373,560
Less	
Current liabilities and funded debt	601,450
Estimated net worth	$772,110
Shares outstanding	4,000
Appraised book value, per share	193.03

Profit-and-loss Statement. This is also called the income statement and has for its essential purpose the difference between the income, or amounts received, and the expense, or the amounts paid out. Rarely, however, is a business conducted on a cash-in cash-out basis; and the stated expenses for any period, accordingly, are made to reflect provision for those obligations which have been incurred but which are not yet paid (portions of taxes, insurance, rentals, etc.) and for the reduction and removal of that part of the property which has contributed to the income. The wear and tear on the fixed assets is depreciation; depletion is the loss sustained through a physical separation of some of the property, and in accounts of oil companies the form taken is the loss sustained through removal of the oil and gas.

ANDOR OIL COMPANY

Profit and Loss Statement

Year ending December 31, 1941

Sales (after payment of royalty)		
Oil	$277,230	
Gas	3,120	
Gasoline	4,290	$284,640
Costs		
Administration, supervision and general expense	$30,240	
Field operations	55,440	
Leases surrendered	18,210	
Depreciation	11,110	
Depletion	46,650	$161,650
NET INCOME		$122,990
Less provision for income taxes		36,900
		$ 86,090

The last three items under costs, it will be noted, are accounting entries which do not represent actual cash expenditures during the period.   They do not enter into the appraiser's estimates of cash income and outgo; nevertheless, they do affect the income tax liabilities.

The reading of balance sheets and income statements and the influence of depletion accounting on oil property values warrant more attention and study than the casual references supplied here.   They are usually more involved and confusing than these illustrations, and they must be informatively considered when they are to be applied in valuation practice.

The Report

The valuation report is a recital from the appraiser to his employer of the facts, his observations, and his conclusions.   Just as the circumstances and the nature of properties vary, so the form and arrangement of the findings are not uniform for all occasions.

No matter what course may be followed in the appraisal of a property, certain facts which exist for every property should be shown in the report, together with enough description so that they are identified and their significant features understood.   The amount of information and the extent of detail will vary with the nature and the purpose of the work.   In various circumstances certain features need not be related.   However, a control list of some kind should be checked and each item considered with the prospect in mind that some readers will be entirely unacquainted with the property, the district, or the purpose of the valuation.   A sufficient description to meet the need of an uninformed reader is, in fact, the test one should always apply.

Engineers' reports gain from conforming to simple and conventional lines.   Many reports demand much detail, but they seldom warrant elaborateness or ornate and striking departures from straightforward and clear presentation.   In size, there is the choice between the usual letter size of $8\frac{1}{2}$ by 11 inches, and the legal size of $8\frac{1}{2}$ by 14.   The legal size is more convenient in many respects, the additional length being especially helpful in the arrangement of tabulated data.   It cannot be placed in lettersize filing cabinets.   The smaller form can be made a half inch wider by having the paper specially cut to 9 by 11 inches.   Paper of this size can be filed and yet provides an additional width that increases the effective space to an area comparable to that obtained with the use of legal-sized sheets.

Contents. Place a brief account of the important features on the first page and, if necessary, on those that follow.   It is distressing to a reader to thumb indefinitely through an extended report in search of the answer. The beginning usually takes the form of a letter, which not only is one of transmittal but also contains the essential highlights — the addressee, the name and description of the property, the specific effective date of the appraisal, the purpose and point of view, a short account of the significant items, and the statement of the estimated value.

Tulsa, Oklahoma
December 12, 1941

Mr. M. B. Whoozit,
St. Louis, Missouri

Andor Oil Company

Dear Sir,

I have examined the property of Andor Oil Company, containing 1 producing unit and about 114 tracts of unproved leaseholds, in connection with your contemplated purchase of these.

The producing property contains 14 oil wells which currently yield 840 barrels gross, 735 barrels net daily under curtailment, and proved locations for 4 additional wells. The unproved leaseholds comprise 12,240 acres. The estimated oil reserves are 3,200,000 barrels gross, 2,800,000 barrels net.

As of December 1, 1941 and based on market value of the acreage and present worth of the estimated future earnings (discounted at an annual rate of 6 per cent) from the producing unit, I consider the property account worth $1,100,000.

Yours truly,

Follow this with a condensed summary by classes and groups of the properties, and this in turn with such descriptions and details as are appropriate for the nature and extent of the report.

Any valuation requires either an assumption or an estimate of what the future promises as the price of oil, its salability, and the various costs. When the engineer once has made these forecasts or assumptions and they have then passed through several hands, they begin to take on the semblance of well-founded predictions or prophecies, and finally even an appearance of fact, unless some account of their sources and their relative importance and dependability has been spelled in no uncertain terms. The extent to which this material and the courses of reasoning needs be disclosed in detail will depend on the circumstances in each report. Pertinent information is never superfluous no matter how voluminous and even though much of it may seem unnecessary, provided it is documented so that it does not impede an orderly reading. The important consideration is a methodical arrangement, put together with excess care to insure a sharp line between the statements of fact and the conclusions.

CHECK LIST

The following schedule is compiled in this form both for the purpose of reviewing the arrangement and presentation of report data and in order to list in one place all the various items which relate to a valuation. Some are encountered in every examination and are essential in every report. Others are met only occasionally and then, usually of small consequence, need only passing mention. Most of the subjects are discussed elsewhere (refer to the Index).

In the Introduction or Letter of Transmittal

Name of the property and owner, with a sufficient description for identification.

Date to which the appraisal applies.

Purpose for which made: for a buyer, a lender, a merger, a tax matter

Highlight features of the property: the acreage, wells and production rate, estimated reserves, proved locations.

The estimated value.

The valuation method: engineering, fair market, etc.

In the Body of the Report

A *summary list of properties,* by classes and groups, with the value of each group.

The geographic situation: topography; nearest railroad point; nearest towns and oil-field supply houses. The sources of water and power.

History of the property: developments and management.

Leasing and exploration activities, in the district and region.

Map. No written descriptive matter can take the place of a simple, clear sketch which shows the area and the situation within it of the improvements and the surrounding developments. A second map can contain the regional features and the position of the property in question.

List each unit of property, by lease number and name.

Area, in gross acres: portions developed and undeveloped; portions proved for production.

Interest owned, and the equivalent net acres.

Expiration dates of nonproducing acreage.

Rental rate of nonproducing acreage.

Royalty rates.

Current daily production rate, gross and net.

Potentials and degree of curtailment.

Well data: Number of oil, gas, water, dry, idle, abandoned, drilling, and suspended wells. Casing patterns, completion data and costs. Undrilled proved locations.

Form of ownership, whether fee, mineral interest, leasehold, royalty, etc.

Contracts against the lessee interest of the nature of farmouts, drilling contracts or agreements, contingent payments out of oil.

Unit project, or likelihood that one will be formed.

Partners, if any, in the property. Joint venture interests call for some details. Names and the interests held by partners, the management contract and conduct of operations, and any other aspects of the partnership agreement which may affect the value of the property or make it unacceptable to a purchaser. Sometimes fixed agreements control the maximum permissible charges for supervision and overhead; the rights of partners to incur charges, the control of the developments, and the drilling program.

Geology: the stratigraphy; reservoir conditions; prospects for deeper sands.

Curtailment areas: the relation of past allotments to the actual amounts produced.

Record of past production, by wells, years and months.

The estimated oil reserves.

Pattern of estimated *future production rates* and withdrawals of the reserves.

The oil: gravity and quality; posted price, sales price; marketing outlets; to whom sold; term of contract.

The gas: gas-oil ratios; reserves and production rates; market; sales return; sales return per barrel of oil.

Casinghead gas and gasoline content of the oil: its treatment, recovery, and sale.

Record of *past gas volumes* produced. This may point to a rapid exhaustion of the gas and approach of the time when flowing conditions will cease and require pumping.

Production and operating conditions: depths; sands and their thicknesses; edge water.

Gas cap: behavior and prospects for expansion.

Costs for drilling and equipping to flow and to pump.

Operating costs for flowing and pumping; for overhead and taxes. Any unusual cost items. Water disposal.

Dehydration treatment and costs.

Oil deliveries: truck; tank car; pipe line.

Balance in operations. When properties are disposed so that operations are not advantageously conducted and are scattered so that centralized control is lacking, then costs increase and values are adversely affected.

Transportation is an important item when a property is isolated and remote from a pipe-line buyer. Account must then be taken of the costs for moving the oil. A fair average rate for 1,000 barrel-miles is $1.20 to $1.70 in railroad tank cars; $0.35 to $0.70 by pipe line; $0.12 to $0.20 by tanker; $0.40 to $2.00 by truck.

Slim holes. Casing patterns of reduced diameters lower the development costs and point toward increased operating costs which result from mechanical difficulties in repair and workover jobs, maintenance of crooked holes, sidetracking, and deepening. Slim holes reduce the values ascribed to deeper sands, as compared with situations where shallow wells, when exhausted, might otherwise be deepened.

Income taxes. Any valuation, particularly one computed by the engineering method, must not fail to reflect the influence of income taxes, both state and federal. It is preferable to calculate and to write this into the final valuation amount on a basis that contemplates current rates. Sometimes this is precluded by uncertainty in the tax position of the client. Notation of this should then be made, and if possible some indication supplied as to the results of differing circumstances in types of ownerships and the range of their influence.

Crude prices. Variations in crude prices affect property values and valuations, the variations being widest in the valuations which follow the engineering method. Unproved acreage and estimates of the fair market value of producing properties move less sharply. The extent of the variations, in engineering estimates, depends on operating costs, profit margins, economic limits of wells, etc. A 10 per cent increase in the price of crude oil generally causes the value of a producing property to increase in excess of 15 per cent, chiefly by reason of the increased amount of oil profitably made available thereby. A cut of 10 per cent in crude prices reduces property values 12 to 15 per cent.

New money requirements for completing the development.

Unusual development obligations, and those which may be provoked by offset drilling on adjoining tracts.

Lease expirations. Term leases expire, either the drilling rights only or both the drilling and production rights. Sometimes the rights to undiscovered deeper sands terminate after a specified period.

Contingent liabilities occur in several forms, usually as payments to be made from certain fractional portions of the oil and gas when produced. Since the appraiser does not concern himself with the nature of the title and since these contingent charges ordinarily are not revealed in the balance sheet, it is in order to require that some one responsible person state definitely and precisely the nature of any undisclosed or contingent liabilities against the properties or the company which owns these. This is best stipulated at the time when the list of properties and the supplemental information are outlined in the appraiser's initial requirements.

The royalty owner. In addition to the rate of royalty, the very character of the owner of that royalty has a bearing on the value of the lessee interest. A single informed and sympathetic owner is preferable to a number of scattered owners, each of whom must be found and prevailed on to signify his consent when the inevitable modifications in lease provisions become necessary from time to time. Two or more antagonistic groups or cliques of owners of fractional portions of a royalty create an objectionable outlook; whatever is approved by one set is opposed by the other. A community lease offers similar problems and difficulties. United States government leases are not looked on with favor by those who fear that red tape and administrative complexities will interfere with earnings.

Anticipated *increases in oil yields* or in the prices of crude oil should not be set up as if they were already realized by a new owner, and thereby made an integral part of the valuation. If there is the prospect for either increased yield or price, it can be noted in the report and, if desired, some measure of the expected benefit can be indicated, and even some nominal weight given when considering fair market value. It is dangerous practice, however, to write an anticipation directly into an engineering type of valuation.

The scope of the estimates. Since an estimate cannot be expected to be correct, it is in order for the appraiser to provide some idea of the upper and lower limits within which it should fall. Thus an answer will be supplied in advance to the question which prudent men ask when entering a new venture, about how badly they might be hurt if matters should turn out unfortunately. It is helpful to a client to have some measure of the effects of fluctuations in crude prices, development and operating costs, taxes, etc. In addition, the outcome of departures of the oil reserves and production rates from the estimates upon which the valuation is based should be canvassed and outlined.

Gas caps of such magnitude that their phase behavior resembles that of distillate pools call for attention to the prospects for good ultimate recovery, in the extent to which this depends on teamwork among the neighboring operators. A large number of scattered small tracts, held by many owners, can tend to defeat the type of cooperative control and treatment that appears to be essential for the best recoveries.

Fair market value. Sometimes the circumstances are such that a valuation constructed by the engineering or analytical method may be construed by a reader as identical with fair market value. It can be pointed out that, in general, an estimate of fair market value of a producing property will range from 40 to 70 per cent of the result obtained in an engineering type of estimate, the ratio varying with the oil reserves, discount factor and the price of crude. A reduction in the crude price has less effect on a fair market value estimate than on the other types of estimates. Reports of fair market value nearly always relate to legal matters, and their form, therefore, should meet court requirements, with a clearly defined account of the facts and with much detail.

Present Worth. Hoskold tables, their use and application, for computing the discounted value of future earnings were introduced in 1877. Many persons do not understand them. Many experienced and successful oil operators rely on valuation reports for help in transactions and yet in doing so they cling to the estimates of future cash profits and ignore the tables of discount factors and present worth because the significance of present worth has never been made plain.

The Internal Revenue Bureau receives many valuations. In matters before this organization a very complete documentary compilation is welcomed — one might say that it is required. There are few inhibitions as to length or elaborateness. The analytical or engineering type receives little welcome, unless it is shown that no estimate based on actual sales records of comparable properties is possible. Engineering studies are in order if made for the purpose of arriving at ratios of values in an effort to derive comparisons with properties whose sales histories are known. In actual fact, too often the question of values in gift and inheritance tax situations is resolved by parleys and negotiations. The government reaches into the air and brings down a high figure. The estate of the deceased then hires experts who turn in a low figure. The two reports are incredibly apart, but finally a middle ground is reached and agreed to by both sides, probably as reasonably correct an answer as could be reached in any other manner, but done in the hard way and a splendid example of a correct conclusion obtained through an erroneous line of reasoning.

Royalties call for emphasis on the estimates of reserves, the prices of products, the timing of the recoveries, and much weight on the ability and energy of the lessee interest in the conduct of the production operations.

Physical Equipment. Two additional matters should be noted. They are not a part of the valuation report but they should be given some attention at the time it is written. One relates to the proportion of the value ascribed to properties that is represented by the physical equipment. Ordinarily this is not segregated and particularized in the mind of the appraiser when he states a value in a property. Occasions do arise when valuations have taken a definite place in transactions or have been the basis of a merger, and at some later date he is called on to provide a division of the valuation amount into the two classes of (1) tangible property (to be charged to depreciation) and (2) intangible property (to be written off as depletion). When a possible future demand of this kind can be foreseen, it is well for the appraiser to compile an estimate at the time the factors are before him and fresh in his mind. It should not be included in the report and need be only an informal memorandum of the surface equipment, facilities, well casings, etc., and their replacement costs at the time.

The Engineer's Statement of His Qualifications. The other matter concerns the last-minute hurried calls from attorneys for a description of the qualifications of the appraiser when some controversial matter is in court. In legal situations such as lawsuits, estate and trust matters, where the appraiser may later appear as a witness or where his report is to be filed as an exhibit, he should anticipate the requirement for a statement of his ability by writing it and having it accompany the valuation report in a separately prepared and signed paper. He should state his full name, address, age, education, training, experience, occupations and jobs held, and any other qualifications, especially those which qualify him as an expert in the matter at issue. If the expression " expert " frightens him, he need only recall the pumper in the gas-separator patent case who qualified as an expert and then testified that the oil came out of the bottom of the device, the gas came out of the top, and the hydrocarbons were picked up and carried out with the gas. No one disturbed the witness with any questions; he was an expert.

In a Report on a Company. Advice is often sought regarding a company and the apparent value of its stock rather than, or in addition to, the worth of its properties. The net indicated value of the stock is ascertained by applying the estimated property account to the balance sheet. However, other less tangible considerations warrant careful attention, chief of which is the character of the management and personnel.

Personal interests of executives sometimes are found to conflict with the company interests. This may be in the form of royalty interests owned in lands which the company operates; or of personally owned lessee rights in competitive producing properties; or of patent rights which return license fees to the owner from the company which employs him. Contract drilling concerns are often closely related to officers. It is not the function of the appraiser to try to correct, or even to find fault with these tie-ups; he must, however, recognize when he is analyzing a company that they preclude an arms-length relationship and generally are not good for the company. Otherwise they would not be concealed so frequently.

Scope of operations affects company values. " Complete coverage " of the gasoline market has been demonstrated an unprofitable objective. One of the best managed companies closes every outlet that fails to show profits.

Some companies plod along and remain in a rut; others are versatile and adapt themselves to the new turns taken by the industry, or they adventure into new avenues even though not along conventional lines. Every company of size has a patent department which normally advises about patent matters and secures the patents which result from the research activities. One company, however, reaches out much further, perceives trends of technique development, and buys patents definitely for the purpose of making money. In this respect it has been highly successful and receives tribute from many sources.

Coordination in activities is desirable. Production in one area and a refinery situated at some distant point is a combination which suffers a transportation handicap. Failures due to lack of balance are observed more often in integrated companies than in companies which are only producers of oil. Companies of the latter type must exercise a greater flexibility, and their being free of refinery connections allows it. However, unwise control of expansion efforts can lead to a producing company with interests badly scattered.

Earnings bear a relation to the value of company; and, no matter how attractive the properties may appear, a prospect of negligible earnings from which to provide dividends is not inviting.

An engineering type of valuation of properties belonging to a company whose stock is actively dealt in, when placed on the balance sheet, provides an indicated value of the stock that is usually two and one-half to four times the price at which it sells in actual transactions. This is why geologists often plunge and lose when speculating in some certain stock. They have computed the value from what they know of the property and have failed to recognize that other stocks sell on a comparable basis.

Companies have traits and characteristics which influence the regard in which they are held by the investing public. Some are smart finders of oil; others are better as refiners or as marketers; and at different periods during the cycles of the industry these various branches exert greater or less influence on a company's success. Some companies pay out their earnings as dividends; others plow back their earnings, and grow and grow but fail to pay off to the stockholders. Excessive salaries burden many smaller concerns.

Growth and activity are important elements. A company may be building up a constantly improved property account, or the properties may be dwindling in importance by being drawn on for production and not matched with acquisitions elsewhere. There is nothing wrong in a liquidating program, but it should be recognized as a liquidation.

REPORTS TO REGULATORY BODIES

In addition to the federal control exercised through the Securities and Exchange Commission, every state except Nevada has an administrative agency of some nature whose duty is to supervise the sale and distribution of securities. Some agencies require that geological and engineering reports accompany the filing of applications for licenses to sell securities, and to some extent they specify the content of the reports.

Generally, the requirements are no more exacting than necessary for a performance of their supervisory task. Occasionally a demand may appear academic and difficult to understand. The appraiser should accept it seriously, comply with it, and anticipate any annoyances which it occasions in his original estimate of the costs for the job supplied to his client.

Examiners in these offices do not welcome short cuts which are based on experience and observation. It is better to spell out in full detail and with extreme simplicity every step in a series of computations. Above all, the unforgivable sin in one of these reports is a failure to disclose any material fact which might in any way serve to cover the subject and to prevent the supplied information from being misleading. Every effort should be made to eliminate distortions or any descriptions or accounts which might be misinterpreted. A good way to help insure clarity of meaning is to have the report read carefully by a layman who has an inquiring mind and is not too bright.

Carry the disclosure of any material facts to an extreme. If a well is producing water with the oil in such volume that it suggests something and especially if it cannot be accounted for, it should be described. It is true that unusually high gas-oil ratios, prospects of gas-cap extensions, and abnormalities in depth-pressure records are highly technical matters which relate to reservoir conditions and are quite beyond the comprehension of the average buyer of stocks. However, the requirement of full disclosure is laid down as a requisite, and it is well to present a broad scope of information. In theory at least, the appraiser is not called on to disclose the fact that the foreman is dishonest or to relate his conviction that the pumper sleeps on the job, because the values of the reserves and not their extent will be affected, and then only with respect to the present operating organization.

In brief, the implied obligation of the appraiser who undertakes a report for this purpose is not to conduct himself as an advocate for the applicant, but rather to supply and disclose informatively all the facts and to interpret these facts with as much weight and emphasis on the unfavorable items as is deserved in a consideration of the entire project.

Securities and Exchange Commission. This federal body has an oil division. The scheduled requirements relate only to estimates of recoverable oil and gas and contain no provisions for valuations of these reserves. Schedule A (Producing Landowner's Royalty Interests), Schedule C (Producing Working Interests), and Schedule E (Oil and Gas Payments) recite the methods used for estimating the amounts of recoverable oil and gas. They are as follows (from Schedules A, C, and E, June 1, 1939).

(*a*) If a *curve method* is used, so state, giving the names of the curve and explaining fully the construction, interpretation, and significance of the curve. State clearly all data used and their application, and furnish actual curve as an exhibit.

(*b*) If the *comparative method* is used, so state, setting forth clearly and fully all the comparative data and explaining fully the reasons for the particular comparison. State how data used were determined.

(*c*) If the *volumetric* or *saturation method* is used, so state, setting forth clearly and fully the various factors used in the calculation, explaining fully how each factor used was determined for the tract in question and the reasons for the use of each particular factor in combination with each of the other factors. Use the actual factors and show the calculation in two equations:

(1) Total oil and/or gas content of tract
(2) Total recoverable oil and/or gas

If drainage area is claimed in excess of the actual area of the tract or part of the tract, a map, showing the drainage area claimed, must be furnished as an exhibit, or such drainage area must be shown on Exhibit A. If any deductions are made for previous drainage of the tract or part of the tract, for shrinkage in volume of oil due to escape of dissolved gas in the oil or to reduction in temperature, and for contained moisture, explain fully.

(*d*) If *any other method* is used, so state, setting forth clearly and fully all data used and explaining fully how the data were determined and the reasons for their use. Explain fully the interpretation of the data.

Estimations of recoverable oil or gas are, in the final analysis, expressions of judgement predicated upon knowledge and experience. An estimation of recoverable oil or gas, however, purports more than an arbitrary determination — it seeks to attach value as a consequence of method. No specific method of estimating recoverable oil or gas is required, but the method used must be an orthodox method, in accordance with an orthodox definition of terms, and the one best adapted to the making of reliable estimations of the oil and/or gas recoverable from the tract in question.

In addition, in Note 5, the person making the estimation is required to give fully his qualifications:

(a) His age

(b) His education, with degrees, if any

(c) Whether or not he is a member of any scientific or professional societies, giving names

(d) The details of his oil-field knowledge, specifying those fields in which he has had experience

(e) Whether his study of the region in which the tract offered is located has been casual or otherwise

(f) The date on which the information contained herein is given, except the information for which a specific date is given

Note 6 requires the appraiser to state his belief that the statements he has made are true, that the opinions expressed are based upon the application of accepted professional or practical principles, and are in truth his opinion, and that no material fact has been omitted.

Form S-10 (for Oil or Gas Interests or Rights) contains

Recoverable Oil in Tract. Furnish an estimation of the total barrels of oil recoverable from the tract and the number of barrels allocable to the smallest interest being registered, and state the name and address of the person who prepared such estimation.

Instructions. The commission does not prescribe any particular method of estimating recoverable oil or gas. Any method which can be shown to be well-founded may be used, but in all cases the data upon which the estimation is based must be submitted, with a description of the method employed and a résumé of the calculations. However, the supporting data required by the preceding sentence need not be included in the answer to the item if set forth separately in the form of an exhibit to which reference is made in answer to the item.

Recoverable Gas in Tract. If value is claimed for possible gas production, furnish an estimation of the total cubic feet of gas recoverable from the tract and of the number of cubic feet allocable to the smallest interest being registered, and state the name and address of the person who prepared such estimation.

State Securities Commissions. Blue-sky bodies, with notes on their requirements in oil property appraisals.

ALABAMA
Securities Commission, Montgomery

ARIZONA
Incorporating and Investment Division, Corporation Commission, The Capitol, Phoenix

Include an engineering report if one has been made.

ARKANSAS
Securities Division, State Bank Department, Little Rock

CALIFORNIA
Division of Corporation, State Office Building, Sacramento

As to a California property, a report by a disinterested engineer. If the property is producing, an appraisal of anticipated future production.

For the sale in California of an out-of-state interest the requirements include an estimate of future production with description of method used; the yearly estimated rate of oil recovery; the production, actual, potential, and allowable; posted market price of the oil and the record of last six months' payments.

COLORADO
Securities Commissioner, Department of Law, 325 State Office Building, Denver

CONNECTICUT
Securities Division, Office of the Bank Commissioner, State Office Building, Hartford

DELAWARE
Office of Attorney General, Public Building, Wilmington

FLORIDA
Securities Commission, Tallahassee

Requires a report from a reliable and qualified person, showing a minimum of 2 barrels of future recoverable oil for each one dollar of the offering price.

GEORGIA
Secretary of State, State Capitol, Atlanta

IDAHO
Commissioner of Finance, Boise

Commissioner asks for specific information at time an application to sell securities is filed.

ILLINOIS
Securities Commissioner, Springfield

INDIANA
Securities Commission, 203 State House, Indianapolis

Requires report of qualified geologist or engineer approved by commission, on the geology, history, production, location of wells, results of tests, and probable potential production of the area.

IOWA
Superintendent of Securities, Insurance Department, Des Moines

KANSAS
Securities Division of State Corporation Commission, Topeka

KENTUCKY
Division of Securities, Department of Business Regulation, Frankfort

Gas and oil enterprises required to furnish satisfactory expert opinions.

LOUISIANA
Securities Commission, Room 216, New Courthouse Building, New Orleans

MAINE
Securities Examiner, State Banking Department, Augusta

MARYLAND
State Law Department, 1901 Baltimore Trust Building, Baltimore

MASSACHUSETTS
Division of Investigation and Securities, State House, Boston

A comprehensive and impartial report by a petroleum engineer or geologist satisfactory to the commission, containing an estimate of the recoverable oil, with a description of the method, formula and factors used; subsurface contour map; estimated future profits; water conditions; life of the property.

MICHIGAN
Corporation and Securities Commission, Lansing

An extensive questionnaire calls for definite and complete descriptions of the properties; appraisals of each; and descriptions of the basis and methods for deriving the values. No appraisal methods are specified, but a classification of the land into producing, proved, highly probable, possible, and worthless for oil or gas is required.

MINNESOTA
Securities Division, 434 State Office Building, St. Paul

MISSISSIPPI
Secretary of State, Jackson

MISSOURI
Securities Commission, Department of State, Jefferson City

Merits of the issue from a geological standpoint must be submitted to the state geologist, who renders a report and recommendations to the commissioner of securities.

MONTANA
Investment Commissioner, Helena

An informal geologist's or engineer's report is required.

NEBRASKA
Bureau of Securities, Department of Banking, Lincoln

Requirement similar to that of Indiana.

NEVADA
No commission

NEW HAMPSHIRE
Insurance Department, State House, Concord

NEW JERSEY
Division of Securities, 1060 Broad Street, Newark

NEW MEXICO
Securities Commission, The Capitol, Santa Fe

NEW YORK
Bureau of Securities, Department of Law, State Office Building, 80 Center Street, New York City

NORTH CAROLINA
Department of State, Raleigh

NORTH DAKOTA
Securities Commission, Bismarck

OHIO
Division of Securities, 612 State Department Building, Columbus

OKLAHOMA
Securities Division, State Banking Department, Box 3082, Capitol Building, Oklahoma City

OREGON
Corporation Department, Salem

Discourages the filing of applications seeking the registration of oil and gas royalties or leases.

PENNSYLVANIA
Securities Commission, Fifth Floor, Education Building, Harrisburg

Questionnaire contains definite inquiries. They include a geological description; also the gauge and capacity of the pipe-line connection.

RHODE ISLAND
Department of Business Regulation, State House, Providence

Report of a qualified engineer or geologist, with complete maps of the properties, showing all wells, producing, nondrilling, and dry.

SOUTH CAROLINA
Commissioner of Securities, Columbia

Maps of properties and structure or field. Also a report requirement similar to that of Indiana.

SOUTH DAKOTA
Securities Commission, Pierre

TENNESSEE
Department of Insurance and Banking, Nashville

TEXAS
Securities Commissioner, Office of Secretary of State

No specified form of report is required, but it must be extensive and must include details of equipment, estimates of oil reserves, lifting costs, etc.

UTAH
Securities Commission, Salt Lake City

VERMONT
Commissioner of Banking and Finance, Montpelier

VIRGINIA
Securities Division, State Corporation Commission, Richmond

Appraisal by an independent appraiser is required; the information to be furnished is left to him.

WASHINGTON
Securities Commission, Olympia

A complete engineering or geological report signed by a qualified mining engineer or geologist.

WEST VIRGINIA
Securities Commissioner, Auditor's Office, Charleston

WISCONSIN
Department of Securities, Madison

Report from a reliable expert acceptable to the Department of Securities, provided the properties are not known to the state geologist. Report must show local and regional structure of the locality, and opinion as to the value of the property based upon detailed data. Also a bibliography of all published data relating to the property in question or to the district in which located.

WYOMING
Secretary of State, Cheyenne

INDEX

Absorption plant, 107, 108
Accounting, 58, 109, 118, 176
Acid treatment, 82
Acquisition costs of oil, 110
Acre, 36
  reserves per, 65
  royalty, 30
  units of costs, 49
  oil yield per, 63
Additional royalty, 32
Administration costs, 127
Administrative bodies, 138
Ad valorem tax, 121, 122
Air lift, 119
Alberta, taxes in, 124
Allowable production, 41
  transferred, 78
Alvey and Foster, 172
Analytical method of valuation, 139
Andor Oil Company, illustrative
  operating record, 116
Angier, J. D., 20
Appalachian fields, 155
Appraisal — *see also* Valuation
  difference from valuation, 4
Appraiser's relation to client, 9
Aristotle, definition of value, 7
Arnold, Ralph, 97, 172
Assets, 177
Assignment of lease, 23
Augusta, Kansas, water drive, 59
  operating costs, 118

Babcock, F. M., 111
Balance sheet, 177
Balanced operations, 15, 184
Ball, Max, 11
Banking loans, valuations for, 7, 160
Barrel, 99
  in the ground, as unit of value, 157
Barrel royalty, 32
Beal, C. H., 97

Blue-sky bodies, 192
Bonbright, James C., 11
Bond issues, 162
Bottom-hole pressure, 17
Boyle's Law, 92, 96
Brace, O. L., 97
Bradford water flood, 88
Brandeis, Justice, describes value, 3
Brantley, J. E., 137
Brewer, Watson & Co., 20
Brown, R. W., 172
Burbank field, 59
Burrell, Geo. H., 43
Butane, 108
Buyer, valuation for, 138, 147, 153
  willing, 165, 166, 172

California, casinghead gas in, 91
  cost of producing oil, 112
  curtailment begun, 79
  lease values, 53
  oil prices, 101
  rental rates, 50
  royalty rates, 30
  well costs, 113
  use of term gross production, 41
Canada, land subdivisions, 33
  taxes, 122, 126
Cap and cap rock, 52, 58, 90, 106
Capital stock tax, 122
Capitalization of income, 9, 139, 166
Capture, law of, 17, 44, 63
Carbon dioxide in natural gas, 106
Card records, 34
Carried interest, 25
Carrl, John F., 63, 97
Casinghead gas, 17, 23, 90, 93, 106
Casinghead gasoline — *see* Natural
  gasoline
Cat Creek, Wyoming, 75
Cemetery lease, 49
Check list for report, 182

197